SAY IT WITH FIGURES

SAY IT

WITH FIGURES

FIFTH EDITION, REVISED

by
HANS ZEISEL

With a new Introduction by
PAUL F. LAZARSFELD

1817

HARPER & ROW, PUBLISHERS
New York, Evanston, and London

For Eva

Contents

PART II. THE SEARCH FOR CAUSES

Author's Preface and Acknowledgments

THIS EDITION has thirteen chapters, three more than the previous one. Chapter 2, "The Presentation of Per Cent Figures," is an expanded version of former parts of Chapter 1. Chapter 7, "The Tools of Causal Analysis," grew out of what was the brief introduction to Part II, of which it is now the first chapter. Chapter 12, "Triangulation of Proof," is entirely new; for the time being it is the modest beginning of a line of thought that I hope can be made richer by the time the next revision is due.

Since much of the text in the former editions had been written twenty years ago and had begun to show signs of age, the book has been completely rewritten. For Chapters 1 through 5 this meant primarily a sharpening of exposition and style. Chapter 6, on indices, however, and Chapters 8 and 9, on reason analysis, and especially Chapter 13, on the panel, have been substantially restructured, and I hope enriched, in an effort to keep up with developments in the field.

Throughout the book I have occasionally replaced old examples with new ones, some of which come from the legal studies that have been my preoccupation during the last decade.

This book has its origin in the work of the Bureau of Applied Social Research at Columbia University and, in the more distant past, in the work of the old Vienna Institute for Psychological Market Research. Personally, I owe a great debt of gratitude to my friend Paul Lazarsfeld, who led our Vienna work and later became the first director of the Columbia Institute.

I wish to thank individually a few of the former members of the Bureau: Cuthbert Daniel and Edward A. Suchman spent many hours in reading and critical discussion with me; C. Wright Mills, with the assistance of Ruby Taylor, edited the first manuscript; Philip Ennis helped in drafting the chapters on reason analysis; and my sister, Ilse Zeisel, checked the computations and compiled the first index as well as the two present ones. Thanks go also to Esther Mulder of Marplan for all the fine charts in this edition.

Old and new friends with whom I have been associated over the years have amply earned my gratitude: Matilda White and the late Raymond Franzen of the former Market Research Company of America; Marion and Virginia Harper and Herta Herzog, previously colleagues at McCann-Erickson, and Lotte Radermacher of the Vienna Institute; more recently my collaborators at Marplan; and last but not least, my colleague at The University of Chicago Law School, Harry Kalven, Jr.

This is also the proper place to recall with fondness my incomparable grammar school teacher, Klementine Enslein, who, in Vienna, a long time ago, taught me to enjoy figures.

Law School   H. Z.
University of Chicago
May, 1968

Introduction to the Fifth Edition

It is worthwhile to reflect on the success of a research text that enters its fifth American edition and has been translated into a number of foreign languages. Having watched Professor Zeisel's plan from the beginning, it is not difficult for me to explain its success and to document the explanation.

The present book deals with ways to study human affairs in a variety of fields—law, consumer choices, economics, public opinion. But it is organized around basic methodological ideas. Twenty-five years ago, they had been tentatively laid out, today they have become classics. Look at the new *Encyclopedia of the Social Sciences,* at the topics that cannot be found in the earlier edition. You will find there extensive entries on reason analysis, panels, and cross-tabulation. The authors practically parallel the outline of *Say It with Figures,* and, incidentally, many of them are alumni of Columbia's Bureau of Applied Social Research, of which Dr. Zeisel has been a valuable consultant for these many years. So this book has helped in developing a structure that today dominates research and practice.

But no formal structure can survive long if it does not come alive in concrete examples, judiciously chosen to illustrate and clarify specific points. And here is a second reason for the longevity of *Say It with Figures.* From the literature which the author has continually watched and from his own ever broadening research experience, he has been replacing old examples with new ones, and has widened their range. Especially noteworthy in this new edition is the inclusion of studies from the field of law, in which Zeisel himself has made groundbreaking investigations, and, in the chapter on indices, the new bridges to the work of the economists.

It is fine to maintain a tradition, but it is also dangerous; new ideas might be overlooked. And here is the third merit that accounts for the book's success. In every edition, attention is paid to ways in which the profession, or the author himself, has added variations to the basic themes, or opened new vistas. First there were chapters on cross-tabulation; later the chapters on reason analysis were added. Now, in a new chapter, the integration of the two approaches broadens the field of empirical causal analysis. This new chapter, on the triangulation of proof, illustrates the possibilities of increasing the power of our analysis by looking for confluence of evidence from independent sources.

Thus this text gives meaning to the often abused notion of interdisciplinary work. In general, problems don't get solved by asking, say, a business research man and a sociologist to work together. What links the conventional disciplines are procedures of inquiry, integrated in the professional training of that younger generation that is not any longer concerned with terminological distinctions. The government, the public-health expert, the politician, the sales manager, the leftist organizer—they all wait for a new profession: the research expert on human affairs, who combines a variety of skills, just as the medical doctor combines training in basic sciences with clinical imagination. Conventional higher education is only slowly recognizing this need; often it puts blocks into the road of progress. If *Say It with Figures* keeps on saying it, it will help to free the passage. The next generation of students may yet see the road open to an ever more expert training in the use of social inquiry, for an ever broadening range of decision problems.

Paul F. Lazarsfeld

Columbia University
May, 1968

From the Introduction
to the First Edition

MODERN SOCIAL life has become much too complicated to be perceived by direct observation. Whether it is dangerous to take an airplane, whether one kind of bread is more nourishing than another, what the employment chances are for our children, whether a country is likely to win a war—such issues can only be understood by those who can read statistical tables or get someone to interpret them.

The very complexity of social events requires a language of quantity. And yet, one who has observed students of the social sciences knows how many have trouble when they want to "say it with figures." I do not believe that this is due to any inherent difficulties. It stems rather from a certain inconsistency in our statistical training. A personal reminiscence of how the present book developed might help to clarify this thought.

After World War I, Professors Karl and Charlotte Bühler directed the Department of Psychology at the University of Vienna. Under their leadership, it became a center for the application of psychology to social problems. We were continuously confronted with topics like these: how do young people acquire "work consciousness" and finally vocational maturity? How does the behavior of parents affect the relationships among siblings? By what criteria do old people, looking back over their life, decide whether it has been meaningful? Is the morale of unemployed men better preserved by dole or by work relief? The questions were the outgrowth of systematic theories about the course of human life and its relation to the social system. But the answers were sought through concrete material: a large collection of diaries kept by young people, carefully recorded observations of family situations, detailed interviews with residents of old age homes, surveys in unemployed communities, and so on.

As an assistant to the Bühlers, I was in charge of training students to handle such material. Little precedent for this task could be found in the tradition of the social sciences. The categories were more complex than those usually treated by quantitative methods; because they were what is called today "qualitative attributes," no standard correlation techniques could be used. Furthermore, the goal was not to find isolated relationships. The results had to hang together, each as part of a consistent whole. This situation led, not to the development of new formulae, but to a kind of empirical work in which qualitative analysis is guided by conceptual schemes and in which each empirical procedure is scrutinized as to its logical implications. After coming to this country, I realized how much it would have helped had we known more about the statistical methods developed by American scholars. In my teaching here, however, I have found that the Viennese tradition is also worth preserving.

Columbia University's Department of Sociology has a special division for the research training of its students, the Bureau of Applied Social Research. Since its inception, we have been bothered by a gap in the available literature.

There is a no-man's land between everyday language and systematic statistical procedures. The empirical research man may get and may give training in formal statistics in our colleges. But those who have observed research projects in government and industry have noticed that these techniques sometimes fail to solve his problems. What is needed equally is an intelligent grasp of what figures stand for and what they can be used to express. The same young research worker who has learned very well to compute a probable error falls down when he is expected to interpret a large set of simple per cent figures, and he fails still further when he must explain his interpretation to a layman. It is usually assumed that no rules exist in this twilight area; the intuition of the practitioner is supposed to provide a way.

This, I feel, is a misconception and an impediment to the progress of social research. In an effort to overcome it, it seemed desirable to present explicitly, and with detailed discussion of examples, some of the procedures which are treated rather casually elsewhere. For, wherever it is possible to "codify," there is a better opportunity to teach as well as to learn. The present book is a first step in the direction of codification. Dr. Hans Zeisel and I have worked together here and abroad, and he is well acquainted with the trend of thought expressed in the preceding paragraphs. The Bureau of Applied Social Research has turned over its files of studies and training materials to him and to this he has added his own experience as research officer of a large commercial agency. Dr. Zeisel has written a text which should stimulate the student, as well as the practical research man, to see the logic behind familiar research procedures and to develop new techniques from such improved understanding.

The examples throughout the book were chosen from a wide variety of fields. A special effort has been made to intermingle materials from market research, sociology and psychology. There is no *logical* difference between the study of voting or of buying. In each of these areas, the final goal is the discovering of regularity in social life. In most cases the examples have been taken from actual research studies; where the didactic purpose seemed to require it, the data were simplified so as to bring out their logical implications.

The reading of the book does not require any preliminary knowledge of quantitative methods. In many places a more systematic approach was sacrificed for the sake of simplicity. For this, and numerous other reasons, the text is by no means a final system. It is an effort to stimulate a certain way of looking at research material, of analyzing and presenting it. This publication is only a beginning in which we hope many others will join, contributing their observations, problems, and results.

Paul F. Lazarsfeld

March 1, 1947

PART I

THE PRESENTATION OF NUMBERS

1

THE FUNCTIONS OF PER CENT FIGURES

THE PURPOSE of per cent figures is to indicate more clearly the relative size of two or more numbers. They achieve this clarification in two ways. First, they reduce all numbers to the range of easy multiplication and division: percentages are usually numbers smaller than 100. Second, they translate one of the numbers, the base, into the figure 100, which is easily divided into and by other numbers, thus making it less difficult to see the precise relationship of the part to the total.

REDUCING TO A COMMON BASE

Table 1–1 compares the sales of the four major American automobile manufacturers in two areas.

TABLE 1–1

*1965 Registration of New Automobiles in Two Areas**

	New York	North Carolina
General Motors	453,569	87,083
Ford	172,748	57,260
Chrysler	128,359	28,442
American Motors and others	31,241	7,424
Total	785,917	180,209

* *Automotive News, 1966 Almanac*, pp. 58–59.

Comparisons are difficult to make on such a basis. Per cent figures (Table 1–2) tell the story better. They help us to see the extent to which the proportions differ in these two areas.

3

TABLE 1–2

Manufacturers' Shares of New Automobiles in Two Areas, 1965

(per cent)

	New York	North Carolina
General Motors	57.7	48.3
Ford	22.0	31.8
Chrysler	16.3	15.8
American Motors and others	4.0	4.1
Total	100.0	100.0
(Number of automobiles)	(785,917)	(180,209)

Chart 1–1 shows the principle of the transformation from Table 1–1 to Table 1–2.

By equalizing the base of both number columns to 100 and by reducing the other figures proportionately, direct compari-

CHART 1–1

Reducing to a Common Base

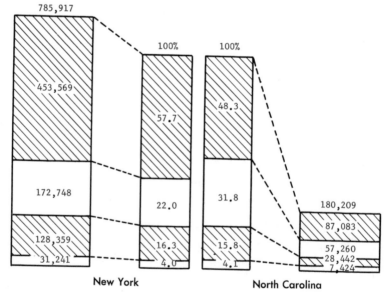

New York   North Carolina

son becomes easy. Thus we can see that General Motors is considerably stronger in New York than it is in North Carolina, while for the Ford cars the situation is reversed; the share of Chrysler and American Motors is approximately the same in both areas.

In this example it was the function of the per cent figures to clarify certain relationships among absolute numbers. But these absolute numbers are meaningful in their own right; for instance, to the individual manufacturers of all these cars. Sometimes, however, particularly in survey work, absolute figures are of no significance whatsoever. Take, for instance, the results of a pre-election poll in a senatorial campaign. Suppose a sample of 3,000 voters had yielded 1,592 prospective votes for the Democratic candidate and 1,408 for the Republican. Taken by themselves, these two numbers have no meaning. The figure of 3,000 is relevant only for the purpose of gauging the statistical significance of the obtained difference. The figures of 1,592 and 1,408 become meaningful only in their relationship to each other, more precisely in the relationship to their combined total:

$$\frac{1,592}{3,000} = .53 \text{ or } 53\%, \text{ and } \frac{1,408}{3,000} = .47 \text{ or } 47\%$$

Fifty-three per cent of the voters declared themselves for the Democratic candidate and 47 per cent for the Republican. To be sure, mathematically the expressions 1,592/3,000 and 53 per cent are equivalent, but 53 per cent is the simpler and, therefore, the preferable expression.

COMPARING INCREASE OR DECREASE

So much for the simplifying function of per cent figures. But sometimes such an apparent simplification may turn out to be misleading. The per cent figures may suggest unwarranted implications, as in the following example.

Suppose company A increased its sales volume from one year to the next from $1 million to $2 million. Suppose Company B, a larger competitor of A, increased its sales during that same year from $4 million to $7 million, and one is asked to compare the sales progress of the two companies. In this case the following two comparisons can be made:

Comparison I:
(1) A increased its sales by $1 million.
(2) B increased its sales by three times that amount, that is, by $3 million.

Comparison II:
(1) A increased its sales by 100 per cent.
(2) B increased its sales by only 75 per cent.

Both comparisons are correct in the sense that they reflect true information. But Comparison I gives the impression that Company B performed better than Company A, while Comparison II gives the opposite impression. Strictly interpreted, the two comparisons do not contradict each other. However, the fact remains that the percentage comparison (II) suggests a development opposite to that expressed by the absolute figures (I).

The important point is that these comparisons, like most comparisons of change, imply something about the causes of the observed change. By saying that "Company A increased its sales by 100 per cent, while B increased its sales by only 75 per cent," one implies that Company A operated under more favorable circumstances or under better management than company B.

It is in this realm of comparisons that the problem of per cent computation acquires a new aspect. As long as per cent figures are nothing more than a simplified description of a set of numbers, this problem does not arise. On the other hand, if increase or decrease is meant to suggest—explicitly or implicitly—the underlying causes of these variations, it becomes necessary in each case to decide whether per cent figures are to be used at all and, if so, on what base they are to be computed.

ABSOLUTE OR PER CENT COMPARISON

Let us return to comparisons I and II. Since they imply contradictory conclusions, one, at least, must be wrong. For which, then, should we decide—if for either?

To be sure, such decisions are not always made on scientific grounds. Those who want to color the picture in favor of Company B will use the first reading; those who want to show how well A did will use the second.

Here, however, we are not concerned with the use of per cent figures as a trick device in support of an argument, but rather with the logical implications of the per cent comparison. What, we must ask, is the exact meaning of the statement that Company A increased its volume by 100 per cent, while Company B increased its volume only by 75 per cent? The answer must come from a consideration of what caused the difference in this particular case. Broadly speaking, two groups of causes will come into play:

(1) *The initial advantage* of each company, such as the size of its sales organization before the expansion, the number of its customers who serve as potential sources of recommendation, and so on.

(2) *The quality of the company's operation* during the year to which the comparison refers.

By expressing the increase as a percentage of the company's sales volume at the beginning of the observation period, we project this thought: It would not be fair to compare the dollar volume increase of a big company with that of a small company;

the proper comparison is the relative, per cent increase. The handicap resulting from Company A's smaller size is neutralized by expressing each company's increase as a percentage of the company's sales volume at the beginning of the period.

The underlying assumption is that had the two companies operated during that year under equally favorable circumstances and under equally good management, both would have increased their sales by the same percentage. If the per cent increase of one was greater than that of the other, the conclusion is justified that its management was better, or luckier, even if the other company's absolute sales increase was greater.

REJECTING THE PER CENT COMPUTATION

Under different circumstances, we might accept the other method of presenting the increase and say that the $3 million sales increase of Company B was three times as great as the $1 million of Company A. This method would be justified if there were little or no initial advantage in starting out as a large company. Suppose the two companies were contractors who obtained business from a small group of customers merely on the basis of the reliability and quality of their work, without regard to their respective size. If we assume that starting out as a larger manufacturer does *not* bring an initial advantage, then we will not hesitate to attribute Company B's greater dollar increase to the superior quality of its management rather than to its larger size. In this case we will, reject the per cent comparison because it would emphasize the wrong aspect of the change.

Thus, either of the two methods of presenting the sales increase might be correct, depending upon the validity of certain implied assumptions.

In passing, we might note that a firm's statement that its sales had doubled from $1 million to $2 million can never be in itself a measure of the quality of the firm's operations. If, for instance, every other firm in this field at least trebled its sales in that period, and none increased its sales by less than $2 million, the increase by $1 million would reflect the lowest increase of all.

THE LOGIC BEHIND THE DECISION

The logic behind the per cent computation is again the same. By allowing a different per cent base for each company, we eliminate the effect of the factor of different initial size, which we want to discount in our appraisal. If no factor of the increase is to be discounted from the appraisal, we will forego the per cent computation.

One can readily think of other situations to which this reasoning applies. Suppose we wanted to compare the growth of two cities M and N, as in Table 1–3.

TABLE 1–3

Growth of Two Cities

City	1960 Size	1965 Size	Change Number	Per Cent
M	1,000,000	1,200,000	200,000	20
N	500,000	650,000	150,000	30

Should we say: "City M increased by 20 per cent and City N by 30 per cent," or should we say "City M increased by 200,000 and City N by 150,000"?[1]

If this growth is a normal increase, caused by an increasing birth rate and a declining mortality, then it will be fair to use

[1] The problem is an old one and has been discussed by no less a person than Galileo. It came up in this form: A horse, the true value of which was 100, was appraised by two people, one estimating its value at 10, the other at 1,000. The question was: Who deviated more from the true value? Eventually Galileo thought both equidistant since 1,000:100 = 100:10. Other participants in the learned dispute considered 1,000 crowns more out of line than 10, the difference being 900 in the one case and 90 in the other. "Letters Concerning the Value of a Horse," *Opere di Galileo* (Florence, 1855), XIV, pp. 231–284.

the per cent computation, thereby indicating that population size at the beginning of the observation period is a crucial determinant of the absolute growth. If, on the other hand, the population growth is not a normal increase, but one due to population shifts in connection with manpower needs, we might argue that the size of the city in 1950 will only slightly affect the number of newcomers. The larger city will not necessarily show the greater increase in population; the city with more new industries and new job opportunities will. Hence, we will say that City M showed a "greater" increase (200,000) than City N (150,00).

THE CEILING EFFECT

In the examples used so far, we have assumed the expected change to be in direct proportion to the initial change: The greater the initial size of the company or city the larger the expected increase in size. There are situations in which this relationship is reversed, where the larger initial size is a handicap for further growth, because there is a countervailing force which makes growth increasingly difficult.

Suppose we go fishing with a net in a lake that is fairly full of fish. The first sweep will bring us X number of fish. On the second sweep we will expect to catch fewer fish simply because we have taken some out on our first sweep and their relative density in the lake will have decreased. On the third sweep we shall expect to catch even fewer, and so forth.

Suppose now one wanted to compare the fishing skill of a man who makes the first ten sweeps with one who makes the next ten sweeps, the first man having removed his catch. Assuming that both men are equally skilled, how many more fish will the first one catch than the second one? Let us apply this rationale to an actual research situation.

Readership of an advertisement is usually measured by the

number of people who have read it as a percentage of all people who opened the magazine or newspaper in which the advertisement appeared. This yardstick has been used not only to measure individual advertisements, but to derive more general conclusions about the readership of different types of advertisements. For example, it seemed desirable to learn how readership of an advertisement is affected by switching from black and white to color. In Table 1–4 are three sets of data which are expected to provide such a generalization.

TABLE 1–4

Readership of Three Advertisements in Black and White and Color
(per cent; each per cent is based on 300 interviews)

Advertisement	Black and White	Color
A	42	52
B	23	37
C	16	32

There are, to begin with, two obvious ways of measuring the increase in readership if the advertisement is printed in color instead of in black and white, as illustrated in Table 1–5.

TABLE 1–5

Per Cent Increase in Readership from Black and White to Color

Advertisement	From	To	Absolute (percentage points)	Relative (black and white = 100%)
A	42	52	+10	+24
B	23	37	+14	+61
C	16	32	+16	+100

Advertisement A, for instance, reached in black and white 42 per cent of all readers, and in color, 52 per cent, a difference of 10 percentage points; or of 24 per cent as against the starting point of 42 per cent (= 100 per cent).

Neither of the two methods of comparison shows an approxi-

mately equal increase for all three advertisements. Yet this is
what it should show, according to the postulate that we show
equal increase for equal cause, namely, the move from black
and white to color in *any* advertisement.[2]

Suppose, however, following the fishing paradigm, we express
these 10 percentage points as the per cent of all readers who
had *not* seen the black and white advertisement, that is, $100 -
42 = 58$ per cent. Taking this 58 per cent figure as the base
(100 per cent), the 10 per cent increase amounts to 17 per cent.
Analogous computations for all three advertisements yield the
results shown in Table 1–6.

TABLE 1–6

*Readership Increase from Black and White to Color
Measured in Terms of Readers Not Yet Reached*

Advertisement	Per Cent
A	+17
B	+18
C	+19
Average Change	+18

The general solution is that the percentage-point increase following the move to color is the greater the smaller the black and
white readership of the advertisement was to begin with. We
arrive at an approximately equal increase if we measure the
increase in readers as a percentage of those potential readers
who had *not* seen the black and white advertisement.

The logic behind this method of per cent computation is: The
higher the starting point in readership the more difficult it will
be to increase readership by any means. Hence, to compute the
per cent increase on the basis of the remaining potential of
readers will be an adequate approximation.

[2] To be sure, it is conceivable that for some advertisements the move
is more effective than for others; but differences such as between 24 and
100 per cent would seem too large.

PER CENTS OFFER ONLY APPROXIMATE SOLUTIONS

The reader who has followed our discussion of where to use and where not to use per cent figures will have realized that in all our examples the assumptions were extreme. In the case of the two companies, either the previous sales volume will lead to a proportionate increase or it will have no influence at all; in the case of the two cities, the increase in population will be either proportionate to the original size of the city—or be not at all dependent upon it. Actually, such extreme assumptions hardly ever fit reality. In mathematical terminology, one would say the model does not quite fit the facts. The business volume of a firm will almost always be influenced to some extent by its respective size; the population increase will always be influenced to some extent by the original size of the population. We should expect in neither case that the increase will be in exact proportion to the factors chosen as a base for per cent computation.

In this sense, per cent comparisons will offer at times only a crude measure. This is the price paid for the great simplicity of per cent comparisons. To the trained statistician, it will be clear that the per cent computation is often only a simple substitute for a multiple correlation analysis. The latter, however, is available only if empirical data are at hand to which correlation analysis can be applied. In our example, we have no statistical data to prove or disprove the assumption that the success of a company is, on the average, proportionate to its size. Our decision to express success in terms of a percentage of the preceding year's business volume would have to be arrived at on the basis of impressionistic reasoning, not through precise statistical data.

By deciding on the per cent comparison, instead of that of the absolute numbers, we merely anticipate the result of an impracticable correlation analysis of sales results of companies of various sizes. R. A. Fisher, the distinguished statistician, called this "discounting *a priori* the effects of concomitant variates."[3] The per cent comparison will be justified to the extent to which this a priori reasoning proves correct.

SUMMARY

The general function of per cent figures is to enhance the readability of numerical findings. Their particular function is to clarify relationships between numbers by bringing them into easy range of multiplication and division. If results from different bases are to be compared, as in most sampling operations, per cent figures become indispensable.

Special problems arise when increases or decreases of various kinds are compared. Whether or not to use per cent figures, and if so, on what base they are to be computed, can be decided only after careful scrutiny of the problem involved. Per cent figures are used here as a crude substitute for regression analysis and other, more sophisticated, statistical techniques.

[3] *The Design of Experiments* (London: Oliver & Boyd, Ltd., 1942), p. 164.

2

The Presentation of Per Cent Figures

From what we have come to perceive as the function of per cent figures, certain rules can be derived as to their proper presentation. The main function of per cent figures, it will be recalled, is to simplify and thereby increase the perceptibility of certain numerical relationships. This simplifying function is often impeded, if not obviated, by poor methods of presentation.

DECIMALS

Let us begin with the problem of decimals. Per cent figures, like other measures, can be computed to any number of significant decimal figures. For instance, 170 is 37.777 . . . , 37.78, 37.8 per cent of 450.

Offhand, it might appear that the more accurately a per cent figure is computed and presented, the better it will serve its purpose. But with each added decimal, the per cent figure loses something of its original simplicity. If the computation of decimals is carried to extremes, the per cent figures will eventually be more cumbersome to read than the original numbers. Thus, decimals tend to defeat one of the purposes of per cent figures and should be used judiciously.

Let us consider the question more specifically. Suppose one were to present the following relationships in percentages with two decimals:

15

Number	97	129	292
Per cent	27.55	42.14	84.88
Base (= 100%)	(352)	(306)	(344)

There can be little doubt that the per cent figures in the second line are not easily read despite their considerable "accuracy." Rounded off, they look simpler and make their point more clearly:

Per cent	28	42	85
Base	(352)	(306)	(344)

Does this mean that we should never present per cent figures with decimals? This would be a wrong recommendation. But in the above example, the decimals introduce what one might call a spurious, show-off accuracy that is normally superfluous. But in the situation below we will certainly allow decimals because here they are clearly relevant, and the presentation problem is only of secondary importance.

Per cent	11.5	11.9	12.4
Base	(9,367)	(10,072)	(10,031)

There are two good reasons for presenting the decimals in this table. First, their removal would eliminate any perceivable difference between the figures—without them, all three would read 12 per cent. Second, these small differences derived from such large samples are statistically significant.

The same difference would be insignificant in a sample of only a few hundred cases. Although it is never a *mathematical* mistake to present decimals, they could be psychologically misleading by conveying a greater accuracy than the figures can claim. If the percentages 11.5, 11.9, and 12.4 were based on samples of 300, instead of around 10,000, it would be much better to stress the insignificance of their differences by omitting the decimals, thereby making them 12, 12, 12.[1]

The decimals should also be retained in cases where a repeat survey is planned, the results of which are to be compared with the first one. Since it is impossible to know in advance just how large or how small the future difference will be, the starting point for the comparison should be measured as accurately as possible.

The general rule to be derived from all these experiences is not very precise, but is clear in its directive: Unless decimals serve a special purpose, they should be omitted. This will increase the clarity of the table and avoid giving a spurious sense of accuracy.

PER 100,000 AND PER ONE

What, however, is one to do if the figure in question represents in fact only a fraction of 1 per cent? Suppose one wants to present the relative frequency of suicides. Table 2–1, for instance, presents the frequency of suicide in various countries as percentage of its population:[2]

TABLE 2–1

Percentage of Suicides in Various Countries, 1962

West Berlin	0.0395	Sweden	0.0169
Hungary	0.0249	United States	0.0108
Austria	0.0224	Netherlands	0.0066
Finland	0.0221	Mexico	0.0019
Japan	0.0173	Ireland	0.0018

The solution here is to raise the denominator from 100 (per cent) to a higher figure, to 1,000 (per mille) or even to

[1] For the counterargument see Hans Zeisel, "The Significance of Insignificant Differences," *Public Opinion Quarterly*, 1955, p. 39.

[2] The data are from the *Demographic Yearbook 1965* (New York, United Nations, 1966), Table 44, p. 762.

100,000, as in this particular case, whichever is necessary to move all but one significant number to the left of the decimal point (Table 2–2).[3]

TABLE 2–2

Frequency of Suicides in Various Countries, 1962
(per 100,000 population)

West Berlin	39.5	Sweden	16.9
Hungary	24.9	United States	10.8
Austria	22.4	Netherlands	6.6
Finland	22.1	Mexico	1.9
Japan	17.3	Ireland	1.8

At the other extreme we should avoid percentages that run considerably over 100. To say that the sales of Company X increased 2,700 per cent over their previous volume makes a formidable figure but is poor statistical technique. It may be less impressive to say that sales have reached 28 times their previous volume, but it states the same fact in simpler and therefore more adequate terms. The general rule, of which the "decimal rule" is but a special case, may then read: Never have more digits in a ratio figure than necessary, and avoid zeros that are not significant.

There are exceptions to this rule. Sometimes the base figure

TABLE 2–3

*Availability of Large Stores in Three Cities**

	Size of Population per Store
Edinburgh	10,000
Manchester	16,000
Coventry	22,000

* After I. R. Vesselo, *How to Read Statistics* (Princeton, N.J.: Van Nostrand, Inc., 1965).

[3] One could, of course, remove all decimals by expressing the suicide rate as *per million,* but international usage—a very important consideration—dictates *per 100,000.*

is chosen not because it provides for standardized simplification, but because it is, so to say, a natural base, as in Table 2–3.

To be sure the figures are large, but they have a direct meaning in this case both to the owners of the stores and to the "population," the consumer.

PER CENTS THAT RUN OVER 100

We must distinguish the situation in which the per cent figures in a column add up to more than 100, as in Table 2–4. A study of the reasons that motivate juries to decide criminal cases differently from judges resulted in the data shown in Table 2–4.

TABLE 2–4

*Reasons for the Jury's Disagreements with the Judge**

	Per cent
Sentiments on the law	50
Sentiments on the defendant	22
Evidence factors	79
Facts only the judge knew	5
Disparity of counsel	8

Average number of reasons per case 1.6

Number of disagreement cases (= 100%) 962

* Harry Kalven, Jr., and Hans Zeisel, *The American Jury* (Boston: Little, Brown and Company, 1967), p. 111.

The per cent figures here add up not to 100 but to 164 because each jury can be motivated by more than one reason. Since the average reader is, in most cases, used to seeing the numbers in a per cent column add up to 100, it is advisable to explain the anomaly in a footnote, or by adding a line giving the average number of mentioned items at the bottom of the column, as in Table 2–4. One should also consider omitting in such columns the customary 100 per cent figure at the bottom of the table, since it may invite the very puzzlement one wants to avoid.

THE RATIO OF TWO FIGURES

Sometimes it will be preferable to represent a two-way distribution not by one of the two percentages but by the ratio of the two percentages, or—it amounts to the same—that of the two original numbers. If A = 80 per cent of the total, and B = 20 per cent, we may characterize this relationship by saying that the ratio of A to B is 4 to 1. There is one particular area in which the ratio statement has become customary, and it is easy to see why. The sex distribution of a population is usually given in terms of the number of men per 100 women, as in Table 2–5.

TABLE 2–5

Sex Ratio (Men to 100 Women) of Alaska, Utah, and Washington, D.C., 1960*

| | Per Cent | | Men per |
	Male	Female	100 Women
Alaska	57	43	132
Utah	50	50	100
Washington, D.C.	47	53	88

* These territories were selected because they represented balance and two extremes.

The ratio method would seem to have the advantage here, because there is something like a *normal* ratio: a balanced population, one female for every male. Moreover, in an imbalanced territory, the ratio provides a more meaningful measure of the deviation: If a young girl is offered a job in Alaska and, incidentally, would like to know her chances of finding a husband there, "57 per cent male" is of little help. But if she learns that there are 132 males for every 100 females, it will be a direct measure of her opportunities. In any event, the sex distribution is customarily expressed in this ratio form; it has become standard international usage.

There are other situations in which the ratio presentation reflects the frame of thinking better than per cent figures. The ratio of officers to enlisted men in an army could, of course, be shown as a percentage of the whole. But here again, the ratio presentation conveys a more vivid picture, as shown by the hypothetical data of Table 2–6, containing three equivalent statements.

TABLE 2–6

Ratio of Officers to Enlisted Men

(a)	Number of soldiers per officer	250
(b)	Number of officers per 1,000 soldiers	4
(c)	Per cent officers of all members of the armed forces	0.398%

There is little doubt that the per cent presentation (c) is inferior. Of the two ratio presentations, (a) is probably the more convincing one.

NUMBERS AND PER CENTS

The greatest threat to the simplifying function of per cent figures comes from the tendency to crowd too many figures into one table so that its legibility is lost. We shall say more about this question later;[4] here we shall confine ourselves to the problem that arises out of the joint presentation of absolute numbers and the per cent figures that represent them. Often a table is considered perfect only if it contains both sets of figures. If there are only two or four columns in a table, little harm can come from it; but if the table is large, serious optical difficulties arise.

The basic question is whether there is a real need for presenting both percentages and numbers. As a rule, there is a simple answer: If the absolute numbers are based on sampling operations, and hence have no direct meaning of their own, it is obviously a mistake to clutter up a table with meaningless figures.

[4] See Chapter 5, p. 59.

All that is needed is the base, the number of cases on which the percentages are computed. The base figure is needed for computing the sampling error to which the per cent figures are subject.[5]

The following Table 2–7 is a fine example of a table—taken from an essay on suicide—that incorporates all possible mistakes of presentation:

TABLE 2–7

Actual and Attempted Suicides in Japan, 1961

| | Actual | | | | Attempts | | | |
| | Male | | Female | | Male | | Female | |
Age	Number	Per cent	Number	Per cent	Number	Per cent	Number	Per cent
Under 20	1,115	10.4	797	11.0	898	16.7	1,299	23.3
20–40	4,904	45.8	3,202	44.1	3,995	74.6	3,892	69.9
40+	4,687	43.8	3,257	44.9	467	8.7	381	6.8
Total	10,706	100.0	7,256	100.0	5,360	100.0	5,572	100.0

SOURCE: Criminal Statistics, National Police Agency, Tokyo.

It presents, without good cause, all the absolute numbers; it does not distinguish them graphically from the percentages; and the percentages themselves are complicated by unnecessary decimals. Moreover, since the author's main point is to contrast actual with attempted suicides, he should have rearranged the columns.[6] Table 2–8 presents the information as it ought to look.

[5] The base figure serves another purpose too: If for analytical reasons it becomes desirable to obtain all omitted numbers, they can be easily reconstructed by multiplying the base by the respective per cent figures:

Per Cent		Number
20	=	153
80	=	612
100		

Base   (765)

[6] As noted, the data are an abstract from census statistics. They have the prime virtues of a primary source, which are detail and completeness. The criticism, therefore, goes to the analytic abstract, by no means to its original source.

TABLE 2–8

Actual and Attempted Suicides in Japan by Sex and Age, 1961

	Male Actual	Male Attempted	Female Actual	Female Attempted
	%	%	%	%
Under 20	10	17	11	23
20–40	46	74	44	70
40+	44	9	45	7
Total	100	100	100	100
(Number of cases)	(10,706)	(5,360)	(7,256)	(5,572)

TYPOGRAPHIC SOLUTIONS

But if the numbers represent a complete (census) count and hence have a direct meaning of their own,[7] then they should be retained. In that case certain typographic devices recommend themselves so that one can more easily compare percentages with each other (and mentally skip the numbers), or compare the numbers (and skip the percentages). Per cent figures can be shown in italics, bold letters or even in a different type size. Where more than one color is available, multicolor presentation

TABLE 2–9

Typographical Methods of Differentiating Numbers and Per Cents

	Italics		Bold Type		Parentheses	
Parallel	50	*18*	50	**18**	50	(18)
Diagonal	50		50		50	
		18		**18**		(18)

[7] As, for instance, the automobile figures in Table 1–2 above.

is a superior means of differentiation,[8] and so is the simple parenthesis.

In addition, one can put corresponding numbers and per cent figures into opposite corners of an actual or imagined rectangle, so that they do not stand in each other's way. Table 2–9 gives a synopsis of the various possibilities, excepting only differentiation by color.

Lastly, there remains the possibility of simply printing two parallel tables, one containing the percentages and their base, the other containing the absolute numbers.

THE PERCENTAGE CHAIN

A peculiar problem in per cent computation and presentation arises with figures that are interrelated and acquire meaning only if these relationships emerge clearly. Consider the statistics in Table 2–10, on the disposition of felony indictments in one of America's major criminal courts.

The table is self-explanatory as far as it goes. But the analyst will ask several questions, the answers to which emerge more

TABLE 2–10

Disposition of Felony Indictments in a Metropolitan Criminal Court*

	Per Cent
Indictment dismissed	19.8
Defendant pleads guilty	59.1
Convicted in judge trial	9.5
Convicted in jury trial	4.4
Acquitted in judge trial	5.1
Acquitted in jury trial	2.1
Total	100.0
(Number)	(4,040)

* The data from Dallin H. Oaks and Warren Lehmann, *A Criminal Justice System and the Indigent, A Study of Chicago and Cook County* (University of Chicago Press, 1967.)

[8] Color is also available on some typewriters, if only for the original.

TABLE 2–11

Significant Relationships in the Disposition of Felony Indictments in a Metropolitan Criminal Court

Total indictments 100%

(1)
Dismissed 20
Maintained **80** ——→ 100%

(2)
Go to trial 21
Don't reach trial **79** ——→ 100%

(3)
Ultimately convicted 73
Ultimately acquitted 27

(4)
Plead guilty 74
Go to trial **26** ——→ 100%

(5)
Ultimately convicted 91
Ultimately acquitted 9

(6)
Choose jury trial **25**
Choose judge trial **75** ——→ 100%

(7)
Acquitted in trial 34
Convicted in trial 66

(8)
Judge acquitted 35
Judge convicted 65 ——→ 100%

(9)
Jury acquitted 32
Jury convicted 68 ——→ 100%

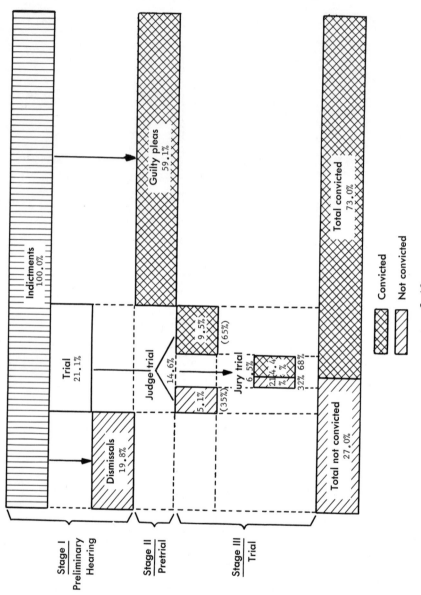

Stage I
Preliminary
Hearing

Indictments
100.0%

Trial
21.1%

Dismissals
19.8%

Stage II
Pretrial

Guilty pleas
59.1%

Judge trial
14.6%

9.5%

5.1%
(35%)

(65%)

Stage III
Trial

Jury trial
6.5%

Total convicted
73.0%

4.4%

2.1%
%

32% 68%

Total not convicted
27.0%

Convicted

Not convicted

TABLE 2–12

clearly from various combinations of the per cent figures in the table:

How many—
    of all indicted defendants go to trial? (2)[9]
    of them are ultimately convicted? (3)
    of those whose indictment is not dismissed outright are ultimately convicted? (5)
    of them go to trial rather than plead guilty? (4)
    of those who go before a jury are convicted? (9)

Table 2–11 answers these and other questions by variously combining the six figures of Table 2–10.

Since Table 2–11, or rather the nine subtables that constitute it, is somewhat confusing, it will often help to present such relationships in graph form, especially when there is a second dimension involved—in this case, time. The disposition of criminal cases is made at three stages: at the preliminary hearing, after the hearing but before trial, and after trial. Table 2–12 reflects these three stages and clarifies the more important interrelationships.

SUMMARY

Since the major purpose of per cent figures is to increase the visibility of certain relationships, care must be taken that this purpose is not vitiated by spurious accuracy. Both decimals and per cent figures of more than two digits tend to reduce clarity and must, therefore, be used judiciously. In some situations special ratios will be found superior to per cent figures, which relate all numbers to their sum total. Problems of presentation arise if both the percentages and the numbers on which the percentages are based must go into one table. Typographical devices are helpful here. The difficulties are aggravated if more complicated relationships, based on shifting bases, are to be presented; only special solutions will help here.

[9] The numbers refer to the place on Table 2–11 that gives the explicit answer to the particular question.

3

IN WHICH DIRECTION
SHOULD PERCENTAGES BE RUN?

CROSS-TABULATION, a device that relates two or more factors to each other, presents the analyst a peculiar problem: Namely, in which direction when setting up a table, should he compute his per cent figures—vertically or horizontally?

THE CAUSE AND EFFECT RULE

There is a guide rule for solving this problem, but it requires some clarifying comment: In a cross-tabulation, whenever one factor can be considered the cause and the other (or the others) the effect, then *per cents should be computed in the direction of the causal factor, provided the sample is representative in that direction.*

Take for instance the cross-tabulation in Table 3–1.

TABLE 3–1

*Book Reading by Education**

	College	High School	Grade School	Total
Read During Previous Month				
At least one book	163	208	30	401
No book	234	624	304	1,162
Total	397	832	334	1,563

* From the Gallup Political Index, March 1966.

28

As shown in Tables 3–2, and 3–3, per cents can be run in either direction.

TABLE 3–2

Education at Various Levels of Book Reading

	College	High School	Grade School	Total	(Number of Cases)
Read During Previous Month					
At least one book	41%	52	7	100%	(401)
No book	20%	54	26	100%	(1,162)
Total	25%	53	22	100%	(1,563)

TABLE 3–3

Levels of Book Reading by Education

	College	High School	Grade School	Total
Read During Previous Month	%	%	%	%
At least one book	41	25	9	26
No book	59	75	91	74
Total	100	100	100	100
(Number of cases)	(397)	(832)	(334)	(1,563)

Mathematically, these three tables are equivalent, but by computing per cents in different directions, different distributions are emphasized and different comparisons offered for easy inspection. It is instructive to inspect Tables 3–2 and 3–3 more closely. The percentages in Table 3–3 yield a simple, if not unexpected, message: Book reading increases with education; 41 per cent of all college-educated respondents had read at least one book during the last month against only 9 per cent among those who did not go beyond grade school.

The message of Table 3–2 is of a different kind: 7 per cent of the people who had read a book during the last month had only a grade-school education, as against 26 per cent of those who had read no book. This is not a very interesting message.

However, the table raises an even more intricate problem. In order to appraise the significance of the per cent figure, one would have to know what the proportion of people with only grade-school education is in the total population. Clearly, if only 10 per cent of the adult population did not go beyond grade school, the figure means one thing. But since all together (334 out of 1,563 =) 22 per cent fall into that group (which is, incidentally, the correct national average), the figure means another thing. But this only shows that what one must know in the first place is the distribution given in Table 3–3: the effect of education on book reading.

The problem can be raised in a different manner. Most survey analysis is designed to replicate a hypothetical experimental finding, as we shall see later.

Table 3–3 can be seen as the answer to an experiment designed to find out how much book reading increases if people are sent to college. To be sure, a retrospective survey table differs from a controlled experiment in many ways,[1] but the structure of the reasoning is essentially the same.

SOMETIMES PER CENTS MAY BE RUN IN EITHER DIRECTION

At times the cause-and-effect rule will fail to provide guidance because of the ambiguity of the situation.

The factors in a cross-tabulation do not always confront each other in a direct cause-and-effect relationship; often their relationship will be indirect. Moreover, the cause-and-effect rule for the computation of per cents admits liberal interpretation. "Cause" may be what the investigator can control. Hence, it will often happen that either factor in a cross-tabulation may be looked at as the causal one, in the sense that it controls the variation in the other factor.

[1] See Chapter 7.

A good example is provided by Table 3–4, which contains the answers from 1,809 respondents to the question, "What is your preferred drug remedy for neuralgia, cold, upset stomach, headaches?"

TABLE 3–4

Remedies for Four Selected Ailments

Ailment	Alka-Seltzer	Anacin	Aspirin Remedies	Others	Total
Neuralgia	107	47	198	24	376
Cold	98	41	401	30	570
Upset stomach	302	60	—	23	385
Headaches	—	242	210	26	478
(Number of reports)	507	390	809	103	1,809

In Table 3–5 the ailment is considered the cause for selecting the respective drug, and per cents are accordingly computed in the horizontal direction of Table 3–4.

TABLE 3–5

Favorite Remedies for Four Ailments

Remedies	Neuralgia	Cold	Upset Stomach	Headaches
	%	%	%	%
Alka-Seltzer	28	17	78	—
Anacin	13	7	16	50
Aspirin	53	71	—	44
Others	6	5	6	6
Total	100	100	100	100
(Number of respondents)	(376)	(570)	(385)	(478)

Table 3–5 answers the question: What is the relative importance of these remedies for the four ailments? In 53 per cent of all cases of neuralgia people chose aspirin; for those suffering from cold, aspirin is an even more preferred remedy: 71 per cent will take it. For upset stomach, 78 per cent prefer

Alka-Seltzer, and for headaches the choice lies evenly between Anacin and aspirin.

But Table 3–4 can be looked at from another point of view. One may ask: To what extent will those suffering from these four indispositions be attracted by the medical promises of each of the remedies? Table 3–6 gives the answer by computing per cents in the other direction:

TABLE 3–6

Importance of Ailment for Remedy

	Alka-Seltzer	Anacin	Aspirin	Others
	%	%	%	%
Neuralgia	21	12	24	23
Cold	19	12	50	29
Upset stomach	60	15	—	22
Headache	—	62	26	26
Total	100	100	100	100
(Number of reports)	(507)	(390)	(809)	(103)

THE PROVISO OF REPRESENTATIVE SAMPLING

The rule as to the direction in which per cents should be computed must be dropped at times because of statistical limitations of the sample. In considering a particular problem, it might be advisable to compute per cents in a certain direction; yet the character of the sample might forbid it.

Consider the following example: During two days of a given week (Thursday and Saturday) observations were made at the hosiery counter of a New York department store concerning the price range of stockings bought and the age of the customers who bought them. Table 3–7 presents the findings in absolute numbers.

The promotion department wanted to learn which price brackets proved most attractive to the various age groups. Price was thus considered as a cause (of attracting various age groups),

TABLE 3–7

Price of Hosiery by Age of Customers*

| Age | Price Range | | | Total |
	$0.59–$0.99	$1.00–$1.29	$1.30–$1.79	
Up to 34	265	12	130	407
35–49	240	140	208	588
50 and over	32	110	25	167
Total	537	262	363	1,162

* Observations were made on a Thursday and a Saturday.

and percentages were accordingly computed in the vertical direction:

TABLE 3–8

Price of Hosiery and Age of Customers

| | $0.59–$0.99 | $1.00–$1.29 | $1.30–$1.79 |
Age	%	%	%
Up to 34	49	5	36
35–49	45	53	57
50 and over	6	42	7
Total	100	100	100
(Number of cases)	(537)	(262)	(363)

From Table 3–8 the promotion manager concluded that only 6 per cent of the lowest-priced hosiery was bought by women 50 and over, and that 36 per cent of the most expensive stockings were bought by women up to 34, and so forth. He forgot, however, that these customer observations had been made on a Thursday and a Saturday, two days on which the age distribution of the customers is by no means representative of all the store's customers. The average customer age on these two days is younger than usual, because it is primarily the younger, working women who shop on these two days: on Thursday because on that day New York department stores remain open until 9 P.M., and on Saturday because it is the working woman's free day. For this reason, Table 3–8 is misleading. On the other hand,

Table 3–9 is correct if one can assume that the young and the old women on Thursdays and Saturdays display the same pattern of hosiery buying as the young and old women during the other four days of the week. Subsequent analysis showed this to be the case.

TABLE 3–9

Price of Hosiery by Age of Customers

Price Range	Up to 34	35 to 49	50 and Over
	%	%	%
$0.59–$0.99	65	41	19
$1.00–$1.29	3	24	66
$1.30–$1.79	32	35	15
Total	100	100	100
(Number of cases)	(407)	(508)	(167)

Elderly ladies, then, buy for the most part medium-priced hose, the youngest group prefers the cheaper stockings, and the middle-aged group shows preference for the more expensive range.

To be sure, if one knew the age distribution of the female customers *throughout* the week, then one could construct a reasonably correct version of Table 3–8 by weighting the various age groups so that their distribution in the table matches the distribution in the store for the entire week.

The lack of representativeness as an obstacle to the cause-and-effect rule is even clearer in the following example. In order to estimate the relative strength of the two political parties before

TABLE 3–10

Party Votes in Two States

State	Republicans	Democrats	Total
A	625	1,375	2,000
B	875	1,125	2,000
Total	1,500	2,500	4,000

a certain election, a test poll was made in two states; 2,000 interviews were conducted in each. The results, rounded off to present the problem in its simplest form, are shown in Table 3–10.

In Table 3–11 the percentages are computed in the horizontal direction of Table 3–10. Here, the cause for the relative strength of the different political parties is assumed to be the state itself, that is, the particular social and economic structure of the state and the political attitudes of its inhabitants.

TABLE 3–11

Importance of Party for State

	State A %	State B %
Republicans	31	44
Democrats	69	56
Total	100	100
(Number of interviews)	(2,000)	(2,000)

The table shows that the Democratic party is the stronger one in both states, but that its superiority is greater in State A.

If we compute the percentages in the vertical direction of Table 3–10, we obtain Table 3–12.

This table seems to indicate that 42 per cent of the votes for the Republicans come from State A, while 55 per cent of the votes for the Democrats come from that state. But a simple

TABLE 3–12

Importance of State for Party

State	Republicans %	Democrats %
A	42	55
B	58	45
Total	100	100
(Number of interviews)	(1,500)	(2,500)

consideration makes clear that the table cannot be read in this way.

It is true that 42 per cent of the *sample* votes for the Republican party come from State A. But the 42 per cent, and for that matter all four percentage figures in Table 3–12, are the result of two components: of the relative strength of the parties in each state and of the arbitrary decision to make an equal number of interviews in each state, although State B had about twice as many voters as State A.[2]

If we weight the figures in Table 3–12 appropriately by doubling the number of interviews in State B, to make it 4,000 as opposed to the 2,000 from State A, we obtain Table 3–13.

TABLE 3–13

Importance of State for Party

| State | Republicans | | Democrats | | Total Number Polled in Each State |
	Number	Per Cent	Number	Per Cent	
A	(625)	26	(1,375)	38	(2,000)
B	(1,750)	74	(2,250)	62	(4,000)
Total	(2,375)	100	(3,625)	100	(6,000)

The percentages are quite different from those in Table 3–12 simply because we have made the number of interviews in each state correspond to the number of its voters. Indeed, Table 3–13, unlike Table 3–12, does show what its title indicates.

THE TOTAL COLUMN

It is customary in survey work to have a column totaling the various breakdowns as the first or last column of any table. Mathematically, this total column is simply the sum total of all breakdowns, and as such it is an accurate set of numbers. But the total column has for the reader a more general significance

[2] Since Table 3–11 was the poll's primary aim, it was correct sampling theory to make an equal number of interviews in each state.

TABLE 3–14

Sunday School Attendance of American Children at
Different Socioeconomic Levels*

				Economic Level				
Attendance	I	II	III	IV	V	VI	VII	Total
	%	%	%	%	%	%	%	%
Regular	49.1	45.5	43.3	52.3	37.3	36.0	28.4	43.3
Not regular	50.9	54.5	56.7	47.7	62.7	64.0	71.6	56.7
Total	100.0	100.0	100.0	100.0	100.0	100.0	100.0	100.0
Total (Number of cases)	(275)	(246)	(568)	(461)	(467)	(150)	(162)	(2,329)

* From John E. Anderson et al, *The Young Child in the Home* (New York: White House Conference on Child Health and Protection, 1936). The economic scale was developed by F. L. Goodenough and J. E. Anderson, *Experimental Child Study* (New York: 1931). I = Professional; II = Semiprofessional; III = Clerical; IV = Farmers; V = Semiskilled; VI = Slightly skilled; VII = Day laborers.

which is usually derived from the heading of the table. Table 3–14, on the Sunday school attendance of American children, will serve as illustration.

Taking his cue from the heading of the table, the reader assumes that the total column is a representative sample of American children, and hence he will interpret it to mean that 43.3 per cent of all American children attend Sunday school regularly. But on this he would be wrong, because the number of interviews on each socioeconomic level does *not* correspond to the relative frequencies of these levels in the country. Table 3–15 indicates the extent to which the distribution in the sample deviates from the actual population data.

TABLE 3–15

Relative Size of Socioeconomic Groups in the United States

Economic Level	Sample Used in Table 3–14	U.S. Population*	Difference
	%	%	%
I	11.8	2.7	+ 9.1
II	10.6	5.2	+ 5.4
III	24.4	15.7	+ 8.7
IV	19.8	18.0	+ 1.8
V	20.1	29.2	− 9.1
VI	6.4	12.3	− 5.9
VII	6.9	16.9	−10.0
Total	100.0	100.0	

* *U.S. Census of Population,* 1930.

The upper-class levels I, II, and III are greatly overrepresented in the sample; the lower levels V, VI, and VII are grossly underrepresented. Since, as Table 3–14 showed, Sunday school attendance is higher in the upper classes, we know that the 43.3 per cent in the total column is too high a figure. If we weight the attendance percentages of Table 3–14 not by the size of the sample as it is, but as it ought to be according to Table 3–15, we obtain 40.0 per cent as the average of all American children attending Sunday school regularly instead of 43.3 per cent.

Two points might be noted in passing. First, that the mal-distribution of the sample endangers the correctness of the total column only if the breakdowns vary with respect to the crucial variable. In our case, if the different socioeconomic levels had not shown variations with respect to Sunday school attendance, the total column would have been correct in spite of its not being representative of all economic levels. The second point to note is that if the total column is not representative of the relative size of the breakdowns, one can, and often should, make it so by weighting its components, as we have done in Table 3–15.

To be sure, there are situations in which the total column is all that matters; at other times, it will have no significance at all.

If the only purpose of a study is to discover the difference between certain groups, say, between the college and noncollege population, as in Table 3–1 above, then the total column is of little interest. But in a pre-election poll, for instance, the purpose of which is predicting the vote of the electorate, the total column may be crucial.

SUMMARY

In most cross-tabulations the question arises as to the direction in which per cent figures are to be computed. The general rule is to compute them in the direction of the causal factor (the variable whose effect one wants to study) provided the sample is representative in that direction. There are situations in which either factor may be considered as the causal one. Related to this problem is the propriety of presenting a total column: It is justified only if it forms a true sample of the population as indicated by the column's heading. If it does not form a true sample, it is often possible to adjust for bias through proper weighting of the subgroups.

4

HOW TO HANDLE THE "DON'T KNOWS" AND "NO ANSWERS"

AT THE BOTTOM of statistical tables one occasionally finds a category such as *"don't know," "not stated,"* or *"no answer."* These categories seldom receive the attention they deserve, partly because their numerical value is usually small. Ostensibly, they all look like interviewing failures, which may or may not deserve to be reported. But the problem is more intricate and more interesting, and it hinges on the exact meaning of these negative responses.

THE LEGITIMATE "DON'T KNOW"

The "don't-know" answer is by no means always a failure of the research effort. It is often a legitimate answer that must be reported like the replies of the respondents who *did* know the answer.

There is, for instance, a type of legal dispute in which the confusion of a trademark, a brand name, or a slogan is at issue. When such issues are litigated, surveys are often adduced to show the degree to which these properties are correctly identified with the company that owns them, as in the example in Table 4-1.[1]

---

[1] See Hans Zeisel, "Statistics as Legal Evidence," *International Encyclopedia of Social Sciences* (New York: The Macmillan Company, 1968); and "The Uniqueness of Survey Evidence," Vol. 45, *Cornell Law Quarterly,* (1960), p. 322.

TABLE 4–1

Identification of Trademark X

	Per Cent
Identified correctly	25
Identified incorrectly	12
Don't know	63
Total	100
(Number of cases)	(822)

The "don't knows" in this table are obviously not the result of bad interviewing. They are one of the three possible answers a respondent can give when asked: "What product or company is identified with this trademark?" Similarly, opinion polls often try to ascertain the state of mind among the citizenry on specific facts or issues through questions such as: "What is the name of the senior senator from your state?" Or "Does the current budget of the United States show a surplus or a deficit, or is it balanced?" The apparent object of the question is *not* the investigator's aim. He knows that the trademark belongs to Coca-Cola and that the senior senator from New York is Jacob Javits; what he wants to find out is whether his interviewee knows it too.

Or, the question may be directed at opinions and value judgments, that is, questions that aim at the respondent's intentions or his views on what ought to be done. For example, "For which party will you vote in the coming election?" "Is our government, on the whole, doing the right things or the wrong things in Vietnam?"

Again, these questions do not aim at finding out whether the United States is in fact doing the right things in Vietnam, but only whether the citizenry *believes* it is doing the right things. All such questions could be asked, and in most cases should be asked, in two steps, namely:

Have you decided whom to vote for in the coming
election?
If yes:
For whom are you going to vote?

"Don't know" is a legitimate answer whenever a question
concerns the state of mind of the respondent, his knowledge, or
his attitudes.

THE "DON'T KNOW" AS A FAILURE

The situation is different when the investigator asks a question
not for the sake of knowing whether the respondent knows the
answer, but in the hope that he *will* know it, because he thinks
the respondent is the best source of information. If there were
a better way of getting at these facts, the investigator would not
conduct a survey to ascertain them. Consider, for instance, these
three questions:

Did you watch television yesterday?
What is your occupation?
In what country(ies) were your grandparents born?

The answers to these questions are obviously not known to the
investigator, and if the respondent says or writes "I don't know"
or "I don't remember," or if for whatever reason he omits the
answer, the interview will be considered a failure.

A QUESTION OF SEMANTICS

One must be careful, however, not to attach the failure label
too quickly. In a mail survey on candy buying (Table 4–2) the
question "What kind of candy box do you prefer for home use?
—for gifts?" yielded a high percentage of "no answers."

To consider these "no answers" a failure would be a mistake.

TABLE 4–2

Type of Candy Box Preferred

	For Home Use	For Gifts
	%	%
Plain box	55	19
Decorated cardboard	6	28
Silk, satin	3	21
Metal	9	16
No answer	27	16
Total	100	100

Clearly, giving no answer can mean: "I have no preference." That the percentage of "no answers" is almost twice as high among the buyers for home use as it is among those who bought for gifts supports this interpretation. The correct solution, therefore, is simply to rename the category "no preference" and leave the answers where they are.

"DON'T KNOWS" THAT ARE INTERVIEWING FAILURES

How is one to treat the "don't knows" that are a genuine interviewing failure? Is one allowed to retain them as a category in the table just like the legitimate "don't knows"? Let us look at an example. In analyzing the fan mail to a once distinguished American radio program, an effort was made to determine the sex of the writers. Since in many cases it was impossible to decipher sex

TABLE 4–3

Sex of Fan-Mail Writers to America's Town Meeting*

		Per Cent
Sex known		82
Male	54	
Female	28	
Sex unknown		18
Total		100
(Number of letters)		(1,390)

* From a study made in 1940, by Jeannette Sayre at the Bureau of Applied Social Research of Columbia University.

from the letter, a fairly large "sex unknown" category resulted
(Table 4–3).

Because of its "sex unknown" category, Table 4–3, is im-
properly constructed; it violates one of the basic rules of setting
up statistical tables:

> Categories must be mutually exclusive, without any possibility
> of overlapping . . . in such a way that any given item can be classified
> under one category, but under one only.[2]

The point is that the "sex unknown" label is shorthand for
"either male or female" and hence constitutes a category that
overlaps with the other two categories.

As a result, the figures of 54 per cent male and 28 per cent
female in Table 4–3 are misleading. It would be incorrect to say
that 54 per cent of the fan letters came from men. The correct
reading is that 54 per cent *or more* came from men. The true
per cent figure could lie anywhere between 54 and $(54 + 18 =)$
72 for men, and 28 and $(28 + 18 =)$ 46 for women, depending how the 18 per cent "unknown" are actually distributed between the two sexes.

The ambiguity is further accentuated if a table containing
such an "unknown" category is broken down into subgroups.
The fan letters mentioned above were divided into two groups
according to the probable socioeconomic status of the letter
writer, which was estimated on the basis of such criteria as
paper quality, cleanliness, letterhead, spelling, spacing, punc-
tuation, form of salutation (Table 4–4). The reliability of this
determination is low, but this is irrelevant for the point we are
about to make.

The casual reader, looking at the first line of Table 4–4 and
comparing 57 per cent with 52 per cent will assume that there

[2] H. M. Walker and W. N. Durost, *Statistical Tables* (New York:
Teachers College Bureau of Publications, 1936), p. 19.

TABLE 4–4

Sex of Fan-Mail Writers by Socioeconomic Status

	Upper Strata	Lower Strata
	%	%
Men	57	52
Women	29	28
Unknown	14	20
Total	100	100
(Number of letters)	(450)	(940)

were more male fan-mail writers in the upper economic strata than in the lower. He is likely to overlook the point that the low figure of 52 per cent is an artifice: It is low because the percentage of "unknowns" is much higher in this group.

We conclude that if the "don't know" is a failure, it should be excluded from the table; per cents must be based on the number of cases that yield a satisfactory answer, as in Table 4–5.

TABLE 4–5

Sex of Fan-Mail Writers

	Per Cent
Men	66
Women	34
Total	100
(Number of letters)	(1,140)

If the proportion of "don't knows" is as large as in this case, it might be desirable to record their number at the bottom of the table by adding two more lines:

Number of letters "sex unknown"	(250)
Total	(1,390)

If the percentage of "don't knows" is relatively small—as it often is—it is hardly necessary to record them. Instead a footnote such as this will suffice:

In the following tables the total number of cases varies slightly because the "don't-know" answers were excluded from them, and their number varies slightly from question to question.

The justification for removing the "don't knows" in this fashion, or the implication of this removal, is the assumption that the failures occurred randomly; that is, that all interviewed groups contributed their proportionate share of failures. This, in turn, implies that if the answers were known, the percentages in the table would not change, because all categories would increase their share proportionately.

If the proportion of "don't knows" is small, their exclusion is unlikely to have any distorting effect even if these "don't knows" are not randomly distributed. However, if their proportion is substantial, the random hypothesis will require testing. The test aims at finding out whether a breakdown of the sample into subgroups reveals significantly different proportions of "don't knows" from one group to the other.

Just what breakdowns should one select for this test? There is no general answer. One should simply begin with those that are most likely to reveal such differences.

REDUCING THE NUMBER OF "DON'T KNOW'S"

If the "don't knows" are not randomly distributed, the remedy is not always simple, and sometimes there is no remedy at all. The best mode of treating this malady is prevention. Failure "don't knows" are at best only an economic loss; at worst they are an impediment to proper interpretation. In any event, their number must be kept to a minimum. A review of some of the situations that cause a high proportion of "don't knows" will suggest some of the preventive remedies.

Assuming that the respondent has no reason to hide the truth, "don't knows" will creep in whenever it becomes too difficult for him or her to come up with the correct answer. In these situations the investigator should help as much as he can.

The fan-mail example, although it served its purpose, is bad in one respect: It concerns an informal, unsolicited response that is totally beyond the control of the investigator. In survey situations, the response is solicited and largely controlled by the questioning procedure.

Occasionally, the "don't know" can be avoided simply by some alert advice from the interviewer. A "don't know" reply to such questions as: "What brand of toothpaste (or of flour) do you use?" is often easily cured by the interviewer's suggestion that the respondent look in the medicine cabinet or on the pantry shelf.

Sometimes a partial answer will be withheld because the question, as asked, allows only a complete answer or none. Thus, in a survey on shoe buying a question was aimed at finding out whether a particular purchase was made in a department store, a chain store, or in an independent shoe store. To ask "In what kind of store did you buy these shoes?" would have brought raised eyebrows and many "don't knows" from interviewees who had too hard a time guessing just what types of stores the questioner had in mind. To avoid such an error, the question was asked as follows:

> In what kind of store did you buy these shoes: in a
> department store?—in a chain store?—in another type
> of store?

In spite of this help the proportion of "don't knows" reached the inordinately high level of 30 per cent. More detailed questioning revealed that the bulk of the "don't knows" was caused by the respondents' inability to recall whether the particular store was a chain or "other" store; purchase in a department store was always clearly remembered. The proportion of "don't knows" was drastically reduced when the respondents were given the additional choice of checking "Don't know whether chain or other store."

ASKING FOR NUMERICAL ANSWERS

The questions that are most likely to bring about a high "don't know" response are those beginning with "How many?" "How often?" or similar requests for a numerical answer. The difficulties encountered here are manifold and deserve detailed discussion. For instance, the seemingly simple question "How many hours did you listen to the radio during the last week?" produced something like 30 per cent "don't knows." But when the question was reformulated in terms of a checklist of three time brackets, the number of "don't knows" dropped from 30 to 3 per cent:

> How many hours did you listen to the radio last week?
> Approximately—less than 1 hour?—1 to 10 hours?—
> more than 10 hours?

Note that this reduction in "don't knows" seems to have been achieved at a price. In the original formulation, respondents indicated the precise number of hours they had spent listening to the radio. In the second formulation the answer is no longer accurate to the nearest hour; it is given only in terms of three frequency groups. But the loss in accuracy is more apparent than real. The question asking for an answer to the nearest hour yields numerical answers, but one may doubt their accuracy. They are likely to cluster around the round numbers 5, 10, 15, and so on, which suggests that they were only approximations to begin with.

One other aspect of this case history deserves pointing out. The reformulated question, when asked of those who formerly had given a "don't know" answer, revealed that a majority (58 per cent) had listened more than 10 hours. Apparently because the number of hours was so large, these respondents hesitated to make an estimate accurate to the nearest hour.

A similar mistake was made when women were asked, "How high is the heel on your shoes?"—a question that resulted in a high percentage of "don't knows." The solution here was to ask the question in terms of three height brackets as defined by their vernacular headings:

> Would you say the heels on your shoes are—high?— medium?—low?

INDEFINITE NUMERALS

Such imprecise numerals as high or low can be used only if their meaning is fairly standardized and does not entail overlapping categories. In response to a question that begins with "How often?" or "How many?" the investigator will at times obtain such answers as "rarely" or "often" or "occasionally." If

TABLE 4–6

Interpretation of Indefinite Numerals

Number of Monthly Movie Visits	Number of Persons Interpreting			
	"Rarely"	"A few times"	"Frequently"	"Often"
0	11			
1	12	1		
2	7	2		
3		17		
4		6	2	
5		4	1	
6			10	2
7			7	2
8			9	18
9			1	3
10 and more				5
Total	30	30	30	30

half of the respondents answer in terms of numbers and the other half in terms of such indefinite numerals, it is difficult to know just how often "often" or "occasionally" is. A problem of translation arises.

In a survey of the frequency of movie going, respondents who had used such indefinite numerals were asked to interpret them numerically, and Table 4–6, a kind of "translation table," was obtained.

The investigator was fortunate in this case to find categories that were almost mutually exclusive. The boxes around the figures indicate the most appropriate numerical interpretation suggested by this table that would keep the class intervals mutually exclusive. "Rarely" and "A few times" can be safely separated from each other; "Frequently" and "Often" overlap too much to be distinguished by separate categories. For all practical purposes, in this context the two expressions were synonymous.

"DON'T KNOW" MEANS "TOO NEGLIGIBLE"

When automobile owners were asked in a survey, "Have you used your car this year more, less, or about as much as last year?" they answered as shown in Table 4–7.

TABLE 4–7

Use of Car in Current Year Compared with the Preceding Year

Used the Car	Per Cent
More	25
Less	14
About the same	20
Don't know	41
Total	100

The unusually high proportion of "don't knows" and the nature of the question itself made it improbable that the failures came randomly from among the other three groups.

A more logical assumption was that the car owners who did not know whether they had driven more or less this year than last might have given that answer because the difference in either direction was too small to be remembered with sufficient certainty. To test this hypothesis, a slightly more detailed check list was given to a comparable sample of respondents. It yielded the results shown in Table 4–8.

TABLE 4–8

Use of Car in Current Year Compared with Preceding Year (Redefined)

Used the Car	Per Cent
More	22
Less	16
About the same	25
Maybe a little more, maybe a little less, cannot say exactly, not much difference anyway	30
Don't know	7
Total	100

The result established the suggested reason for the "don't know" response. The respondents who answered, "Maybe a little more, etc." clearly corresponded to the bulk of the "don't knows" in the comparable sample (Table 4–7).

Again, the additional choice on the check list drastically curtailed the number of "don't knows."

FACILITATING THE RECALL

There is still another typical reason for the occasional failure to respond to a numerical question. When housewives are asked a question such as "How many cans of cleanser did you buy during the last month?" a considerable number of them answer, "I don't know." This number can be greatly reduced if the question is broken down into two parts:

(1) How often did you buy cleanser during the last month?
(2) How many cans of cleanser do you usually buy at one time?

In this form the question provides a guide for the respondent's memory and eliminates the need for mental calculation. It has, moreover, the advantage of providing additional data: We now have information on the frequency of purchase *and* the average size of each purchase, whereas the first question could yield only the product of both, the over-all amount.

REDUCING THE LEGITIMATE "DON'T KNOWS"

So far we have discussed only the reduction of the failure "don't knows." Even when they are a legitimate response, they are occasionally an unsatisfactory one because they form a catchall for a variety of positions that the investigator might want to clarify.

This is particularly true for questions that try to elicit opinions on a complicated issue. During World War II, the U.S. Office of War Information asked a question concerning the conduct of the war. Since a considerable number of "don't knows" was expected, the interviewers were instructed to follow up with the question: "Why do you say you do not know?" The answers to this follow-up question fell into the following pattern:

(1) *General lack of exposure:* I've had so little time to read about those things—my radio hasn't been working—have not had a chance to read the news—can't read so good—don't read much—don't listen to it—haven't heard much about it.

(2) *Information for decision is not available to the public:* If I knew the situation I would know how to answer—lack of information—people are in no condition to answer—we don't know what is best—don't know enough to make a decision—don't know enough about this war.

(3) *Can't make up mind:* Have weighed both sides, but haven't made up my mind—have not been able to make up my mind—

there is so much to consider—I've thought about it, but can't make up my mind—it takes a lot of thinking to decide—I think one thing one time and then read something which changes my mind so I don't know.

(4) *No reason given:* Don't know—I wouldn't know—couldn't answer intelligently—hard to answer.

In category (2), some of the interviewees went even further and specified the information they thought they needed to make up their mind.

As a rule, however, one can argue that questions which yield a high "don't know" response with so complicated a substructure should perhaps not be asked in the first place. At least an effort should be made in such cases to determine whether the "don't know" response reflects primarily a lack of essential information or a lack of decision.[3]

EVASIVE "DON'T KNOWS"

Criminologists claim that the polygraph, through a simultaneous measurement of such things as perspiration, heartbeat, and respiration, is able to distinguish truthful from false testimony. The technique of interviewing is far from a similar state of perfection, but sometimes false or evasive "don't knows" can be identified and even corrected with the help of a statistical lie detector.[4]

At the beginning of World War II a survey was made of the

[3] Another instance of this ambiguity was found by Dunette, Uphoff, and Aylward, "The Effect of Lack of Information on the Undecided Response in Attitude Surveys," *Journal of Applied Psychology*, 1956, pp. 150–53: "Undecided responses . . . stem from two major sources: persons who lack sufficient information on the point in question to form an attitude . . . and, persons who *do* have knowledge of the point in question, have considered the pros and cons, and have arrived at a neutral or 'undecided' position."

[4] The term has found acceptance. See the interesting study by David Gold, "The Lie Detector; An Application to . . . a Voting Study," *American Sociological Review*, 1955, p. 527.

rice-purchasing habits of American housewives. It was conducted by mail and the housewives were asked to classify themselves as to their annual family income by checking one of the
following groups:[5]

□ Under $1,000
□ $1,000–$1,999
□ $2,000–$2,999
□ $3,000 and over

Approximately 12 per cent of all respondents did not answer
the question. Offhand, there was no clue as to whether this
failure was due to negligence, occurred at random regardless of
income, or whether other reasons were operative. The following
table (Table 4–9) from the survey suggests the correct answer.
It relates income to the results of the question "Do you usually
buy rice in bulk, branded, or both ways?"

TABLE 4–9

Housewives Buying Rice in Bulk or Branded, by Income, 1939

	Under $1,000	$1,000–$1,999	$2,000–$2,999	Over $3,000	Income Not Stated
	%	%	%	%	%
Brand only	32	43	49	56	55
Bulk only	49	34	25	15	16
Both	19	23	26	29	29
Total	100	100	100	100	100
(Number of cases)	(237)	(715)	(364)	(266)	(212)

The table shows a clear relationship between income and
buying rice branded or in bulk. The higher the income the
greater the proportion of housewives who buy branded rice; the
lower the income the more bulk rice is bought. Since bulk rice
is cheaper, the result is not surprising. But the point that interests us is that those housewives who did not state their income

[5] The survey was conducted in 1939, hence the relatively low income
brackets.

exhibit almost the same buying pattern as the group in the over-$3,000 bracket. The similarity was so striking that it suggested the desire not to divulge a top income as a motive for the failure to classify by income. This becomes understandable if we learn that these housewives were offered a small reward for their cooperation.

The point is further corroborated by another table from that survey. The average price paid for branded-rice by the various income groups yielded the figures in Table 4–10.

TABLE 4–10

Average Price Paid for Branded Rice by Various Income Groups

Income	Cents
Under $1,000	9
$1,000–$1,999	10
$2,000–$3,000	13
Over $3,000	14
Income not stated	15

Again, the income-not-stated group behaved most like the over-$3,000 group.

A more complicated evasive pattern emerged from the analysis of a survey on family relations. Teen-agers were asked whether their parents had punished them physically during their early childhood. A rather high percentage of these youngsters answered, "I don't remember." The high percentage by itself did not necessarily point toward some hidden motive, but because of the nature of the topic, it raised suspicion. Hence, the standard procedure recommended for such situations was applied: An effort was made to learn whether the frequency of memory failures was related to some significant characteristic of these children. Table 4–11 reveals such a relationship.

The table shows first that teen-agers are more likely to have confidence in their parents if they have *not* been corporally punished, than if they have been so punished (50 versus 45

TABLE 4–11

Corporal Punishment and Confidence in Parents

Children Say They Have More Confidence—	Children Say They Have or Have Not Been Corporally Punished		
	Not punished	Punished	Don't remember
	%	%	%
In parents	50	45	34
In other persons	32	42	50
Cannot state	18	13	16
Total	100	100	100
(Number of cases)	(282)	(412)	(165)

per cent). The surprising and revealing point, however, is that the lowest degree of confidence in parents is shown by those (34 per cent) who profess not to remember if their parents had beaten them. If these "don't remembers" had been random failures, the frequency of "Have more confidence in parents" should have lain somewhere between the 50 and 45 per cent figures in the top line of the first two columns. Since the figure lies far outside this range, the suspicion arose that the "don't remember" was, at times, a conscious or unconscious cover-up for the deeply resented, and perhaps repressed, fact that they had been beaten by their parents. Subsequent inquiries confirmed the hypothesis.

THE CENSUS ELIMINATES 207,000 "DON'T KNOWS"

At some time the Census Bureau, in its tables on the age of the United States population, showed some 169,000 of the population as "age unknown." The U.S. Census for 1910, for instance, contained the data shown in Table 4–12.

Although the "unknown" category was small enough, it constituted both a nuisance and an impropriety—a nuisanse because in all tables based on age breakdowns an extra column had to be tabulated, checked, and printed: an impropriety because it was an overlapping category.

TABLE 4–12

United States Age Distribution, 1910*

Age	Per Cent	
Under 5	11.6	
5–9	10.6	
10–14	9.9	
.	.	
.	.	
.	.	
70–74	1.2	
75–79	0.7	
80–84	0.3	
85 and over	0.2	
Unknown	0.2	(actually 0.18 = 169,055)
Total	100.0	

(Number of
cases)   (91,972,266)

* *Statistical Abstract of the United States, 1941*, p. 44.

For the purposes of a straight tabulation, it might be sufficient to assume randomness, and to distribute the failures proportionately among the other age groups. This procedure would not do in breakdowns, however, because it might easily assign to some heads of families an age "under 5."

Moreover, the Bureau of the Census discovered that these "age unknowns" were not random failures but occurred more frequently in groups of particular age ranges, e.g., among lodgers and hotel guests. Also, a disproportionately high number were infants under one year whose exact age in terms of months was not indicated.

The Bureau of the Census, therefore, in the Census of 1940,[6] set to work to estimate the individual age of each of the 207,211 persons whose age was unknown.

The method used was essentially the following: Briefly, the age of a person was estimated on the basis of other information on his census card such as marital status, school attendance, em-

[6] C. Edwards Deming, *The Elimination of Unknown Ages in the 1940 Population Census*, U.S. Department of Commerce, January 1942.

ployment status, and age of other members in the family. A fairly accurate estimate could be made for school children if their grade was known. An estimate of age of married people was made from the age of the spouse on the basis of correlation tables. Where the age could be ascertained only within certain limits, care was taken to distribute estimates over this range so as to avoid clusters around the multiples of five. It should be added that an experimental comparison of 4,000 age estimates against actual age revealed that approximately 45 per cent were estimated correctly or within one year of the true age. Only 19 per cent were in error by more than five years.

SUMMARY

The frequently overlooked "don't knows" or "no answers" at the bottom of statistical tables may be either a legitimate category or an interviewing failure.

If they are a legitimate category—because we want to know whether or not the respondent knows the answer—they have to be included in the tabulation, and any efforts to reduce or avoid these "don't knows" would constitute bias. If the "don't know" answer represents an interviewing failure—because we want the respondent to remember—a different solution is required. The first job is to reduce these failures to a minimum through proper interviewing techniques. The failures that remain despite all efforts offer this basic problem of interpretation: Do they occur at random with equal frequency within all groups of respondents? If they do, these failures may be properly excluded from the tabulation. Often, however, some subgroups of the sample will tend to produce—unconsciously and even consciously—more "failures" than others; in that case one must try to estimate the amount of bias through proper cross-tabulation and, if possible, recover the hidden meaning of these "don't knows."

5

Tables of More Than Two Dimensions

THE PROBLEM OF REDUCTION

A TWO-DIMENSIONAL TABLE, that is, one that tabulates two factors against each other, offers, if properly prepared, no difficulties of presentation. But if tables of three or more dimensions are presented in the traditional manner, the clarity required of a good statistical table is threatened.

In Table 5–1, three factors are tabulated against each other. The Table reports attitudes of shoppers toward the proposed night (late evening) opening of a department store.[1] The attitude is tabulated against two other factors: the frequency with which these respondents buy in the store (the second dimension), and the frequency with which they shop at night (the third dimension).

Such a three-dimensional table is actually the composite of three two-dimensional tables printed side by side; the resulting loss in clarity is considerable even if, as in the present case, the absolute numbers are reduced to one base figure at the bottom of each column. For example, if we want to learn how the attitude toward night opening is affected by the frequency of buying in this store, we must read the figures in the fourth, eighth, twelfth, and sixteenth column.

---

[1] From a survey conducted for a New York department store by the Bureau of Applied Social Research of Columbia University.

TABLE 5-1

Public's Attitude Toward Keeping XX Store Open After 5:30 P.M., by Frequency of Shopping at XX and Frequency of Night Shopping

Frequency of Shopping at XX Store

Attitude Toward Keeping XX Store Open	Frequently				Occasionally				Never				Total			
	At least every other week	Less often	Never	Total	At least every other week	Less often	Never	Total	At least every other week	Less often	Never	Total	At least every other week	Less often	Never	Total
Favor night opening	% 90	% 58	% 20	% 45	% 85	% 51	% 11	% 42	% 41	% 24	% 9	% 23	% 76	% 48	% 15	% 40
Do not favor it	10	42	80	55	15	49	89	58	59	76	91	77	24	52	85	60
Total	100	100	100	100	100	100	100	100	100	100	100	100	100	100	100	100
(Number of cases)	(115)	(176)	(300)	(591)	(105)	(103)	(171)	(379)	(74)	(80)	(97)	(251)	(294)	(359)	(568)	(1,221)

REDUCING ONE DIMENSION

The problem is one of geometric logic: How can three dimensions be presented in a two-dimensional table? The solution must lie in eliminating one dimension, that is, in reducing the several figures of a column to one figure. In the language of geometry: by reducing a line to a point.

Let us take the last column of Table 5–1 as an example, reproducing it as Table 5–2.

TABLE 5–2

Attitude Toward Night Opening

	Per Cent
Favor it	40
Do not favor it	60
Total	100
(Number of cases)	(1,221)

The information conveyed in this table can be written in one figure, without any loss, by stating that 40 per cent of the respondents favor night opening. Few readers will have difficulties seeing automatically the complementary figure, the 60 per cent who do *not* favor it.

If we apply this principle to all sixteen columns of Table 5–1 we obtain a three-dimensional table that offers all optical advantages of a two-dimensional table. In Table 5–3, each of the sixteen figures represents the per cent of respondents in the particular group who favor night opening. The unwritten proportion of respondents who do *not* favor night opening is always the difference between each of these per cent figures and 100.

With the exception of the base numbers,[2] this relatively small table contains the same information as Table 5–1. Unlike that table, however, it tells its story with the utmost simplicity.

[2] For the treatment of that problem, see Chapter 2.

TABLE 5–3

Per Cent of Public Favoring Keeping XX Store Open After 5:30 P.M. by Frequency of Shopping at XX and Frequency of Night Shopping

(each figure indicates the per cent of respondents in
each group who favor night opening)

Frequency of Night Shopping	Frequency of Shopping at XX			Total
	Frequently	Occasionally	Never	
At least every other week	90	85	41	76
Less often	58	51	24	48
Never	20	11	9	15
Total	45	42	23	40

The first number in Table 5–3 indicates, then, that among the customers who shop at XX *frequently* (above) and shop at night *at least every other week* (left), 90 per cent favor night opening.

In this table one can easily perceive all important relationships: Both frequency of shopping at XX and frequency of night shopping affect attitudes toward night opening of that store. And, as one might expect, of the two, frequency of night shopping is the more important influence: The Total column at right drops from 76 to 15 per cent, while the Total row at the bottom moves only from 45 to 23 per cent.

THE PRINCIPLE ILLUSTRATED

This somewhat unusual but indispensable method of presenting multidimensional tables needs further illumination. Table 5–4 is an example of a simple three-dimensional table:

TABLE 5–4

Education by Sex and Income

Educational Level	Men		Women	
	High Income	Low Income	High Income	Low Income
	%	%	%	%
More than high school	50	20	40	10
High school or less	50	80	60	90
Total	100	100	100	100

If these four columns are rearranged spatially in the form of a cube, Chart 5–1 is obtained:

CHART 5–1

Per Cent Having More Than High School Education

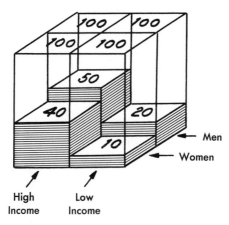

A bird's-eye view of this cube offers a square, four-fold table that contains all relevant data:

TABLE 5–5

Per Cent in Each Group Having More Than High School Education

	High Income	Low Income
Men	50	20
Women	40	10

The complementing percentages, representing those having high school education or less, are represented in the chart by the upper, empty part of the column: the difference of each known percentage from the total 100 per cent.

The per cent figure is not the only way of presenting a column of two numbers through a single number. It will be remembered from Chapter 1 that in some cases the ratio method may be used to perform the same function.[3]

MAKING A DICHOTOMY

But what is one to do if the crucial measure does not naturally fall into two groups, such as those who do and those who don't? One of the things one can sometimes do is to *make* a dichotomy of a distribution that may consist of three or more groups as in Table 5–6.

TABLE 5–6

Frequency of Eating Cold Cereal, by Sex and Community Size

Eat Cold	Urban		Rural	
Cereal	Men	Women	Men	Women
	%	%	%	%
Daily	27	35	39	31
Frequently	18	22	27	20
Occasionally	6	11	14	10
Never	49	32	20	39
Total	100	100	100	100
(Number of cases)	(199)	(201)	(100)	(99)

Here one could combine, for instance, the first three groups and with some loss in detail arrive at the dichotomy of those who do eat cereal and those who never eat cereal. Actually, there are two more ways of making a dichotomy. One could distinguish the first line from the sum of the remaining three columns (daily cereal eaters versus all others); finally, one could combine the first and second lines (those who eat cereal daily or at least frequently) and contrast them with the third and fourth (those who eat it never or at best occasionally). All three possibilities are spelled out in Table 5–7; note that, although the level of the percentages changes depending on the chosen dichotomy, their

[3] A distribution of 60 per cent men and 40 per cent women can be represented by the number 150, indicating the number of men per 100 women (page 20).

relative standing changes little; in fact, their rank order remains the same.[4]

TABLE 5–7

Three Measures of Eating Cold Cereal
(per cent in each group)

Eat Cold Cereal	Urban		Rural	
	Men	Women	Men	Women
Daily	27%	35%	39%	31%
Rank	*4*	*2*	*1*	*3*
Daily or at least frequently	45%	57%	66%	51%
Rank	*4*	*2*	*1*	*3*
At least occasionally	51%	68%	80%	61%
Rank	*4*	*2*	*1*	*3*

USING AN AVERAGE TO REPRESENT THE COLUMN

If the column consists of a variable that permits counting, an average—usually the mean—may conveniently represent the column, as in Table 5–8.

TABLE 5–8

Frequency of Magazine Reading in Two Cities, by Economic Status
(per cent of people reading the indicated number of magazines)

Number of magazines read:	City M		City N	
	Upper economic strata	Lower economic strata	Upper economic strata	Lower economic strata
	%	%	%	%
0	25	40	16	30
1	23	36	29	42
2	39	18	41	25
3	9	6	10	1
4	4	—	3	2
5	1	—	1	—
Total	100	100	100	100
(Number of persons)	(1,199)	(1,792)	(1,001)	(2,101)

[4] This interchangeability of different indices for the same concept is a widespread phenomenon which greatly reduces in analogous situations the importance of selecting the best index, because any number of them will prove interchangeable.

Differences in magazine reading as between the two cities and the two economic groups cannot be easily discerned; there are simply too many figures. By computing the average number of magazines read per person in each of the six groups, we obtain Table 5–9.

TABLE 5–9

Average Number of Magazines Read per Person in Two Cities, by Economic Status

	Upper economic strata	Lower economic strata
City M	1.49	0.90
City N	1.58	1.03

Now we can see quite clearly that reading in the upper economic strata is about 50 per cent higher than in the lower strata, and in each group—hence also in the city as a whole—City N reads slightly more than City M.

The use of an average to represent a distribution is particularly indicated if the categories of the distribution do not form a natural continuum because they were collected in a form designed to aid the respondent's recall. In the already mentioned survey of rice consumption, housewives were asked how frequently they served rice in various forms. To facilitate their answer, they were given a check list:

About—
☐ two or three times a week
☐ once a week
☐ two or three times a month
☐ once a month or less often

The answers had to be brought to the common denominator of the longest serving interval, the period of one month. On that basis, with some approximating and rounding off, one might weight the four answers by 20, 8, 2½, and ½, respectively. The table then can be presented in terms of servings per month (Table 5–10).

TABLE 5–10

*Frequency of Serving Rice Dishes
in the West of the United States*

	Average Per Month
As a dessert	4.9
In mixed dishes	1.9
Plain	1.6
In a soup	1.4
Total (in any form)	9.8

RANK ORDERS

Sometimes all we have of a distribution is a rank order: Which television channel do you listen to most? Which comes next? Or: Which brand do you buy (or sell) most frequently? Which next? It is not easy to reduce a column of rank orders to one figure. In the absence of better information, there is always the possibility of arbitrary weights: If there are four ranks one could weight the first rank by 4, the second by 3, and so forth. Such a procedure is based on the twofold assumption that *these* are the proper weights and that they are a good approximation for all units.

The problem of rank-order weights can be better understood if these weights are derived from empirical data, as in the following example.

A sample of 100 grocers in Birmingham, Alabama, was asked, "What brands of bread do you sell? State them in the order of the approximate dollar volume they represent." Their answers are tabulated in Table 5–11.

TABLE 5–11

Number of Grocers Reporting Various Bread Brands as the Leading Brand, Second, and so on*

Brands	Leading Brand	Second Place	Third Place	Fourth or Later Place	Total
A	52	29	13	1	95
B	28	25	22	19	94
C	13	11	25	38	87
D	5	12	15	13	45
E	1	15	14	15	45
All others	1	8	11	14	34
Total	100	100	100	100	100

* From a survey made by the Market Research Company of America.

We are, of course, concerned with the last, the Total column. In its present form, it simply gives the per cent (since there are altogether 100 grocers the numbers are equivalent to percentages) of stores that sell the particular brand of bread; no weight is given to whether the brand sells first or last. If we look at the total picture of brands A and B, it is quite clear that A sells better than B—it is mentioned almost twice as often in first place as B—yet the Total column shows them close, at 95 and 94 per cent, respectively. In this case the grocers themselves allowed a more accurate assessment, by answering the additional question as to the approximate percentage each brand occupied. The values they gave for each rank did not differ too widely, and so it was decided to average these rank-percentages as follows:

Rank	Per Cent of Total Sales
1	40
2	31
3	17
4 and later	12
Total	100

If we perform the multiplication for Table 5–11 (and also allow equal weights for every store irrespective of size differences) we obtain for the various brands:

Bread Brands	Approximate Per Cent Share of Market
A	32
B	25
C	17
D	10
E	9
Others	7
Total	100

THE "ITEM MENTIONED FIRST"

Occasionally the structure of the ranked answers will permit a much simpler solution. Today we have all kinds of research methods that attack this problem head on with great power, methods which in the early years of broadcasting were not available. At that time the research department of the National Broadcasting Company,[5] developed a simple and surprisingly successful device. In every county of the United States a representative sample of families was asked to record all radio stations to which they *listened regularly* and also the one station they *listened to most.*

In some fifty-odd cities it was possible to compare the results of this method with actual station shares of total listening time, developed independently by a more complicated and more costly method. Table 5–12 compares the independently established

TABLE 5–12

Station Shares of Daytime Radio Audience in New York City

	Station "Listened to Most"	Independently Established Station Share
	%	%
WCBS	24	25
WNBC	17	18
WJZ	12	13
WOR	14	14
WNEW	10	10
Other stations	23	20
Total	100	100

[5] Hugh M. Beville, who was then its director, with Kenneth Greene.

station shares of total listening time with those based on the question: "To which one station do you listen most?"

As it turned out, the proportion of homes that record a particular station as "listened to most" is almost identical with that station's share of audience.

In situations like these, a single-answer question will provide a useful short-cut that avoids the cumbersome multiple-answer approach, requiring a complicated and sometimes almost impossible weighting procedure.

SYMMETRIC TRICHOTOMIES

There is a type of symmetric distribution, frequently encountered in survey work, where the two marginal categories have opposing value signs, while the middle category represents a zero category or indifference area. They form such patterns as more–same–less, or like–indifferent–dislike: (per cent +), (per cent =), (per cent −).

In many of these situations the natural and simplest contraction of the trichotomy will be its mathematical resolution, (per cent +) minus (per cent −), the percentage of the *more* minus the percentage of the *less,* or the percentage of the *positive* minus the percentage of the *negative*—the middle, zero category being without value.

This balance index will be positive as long as the (per cent +) is larger than the (per cent −), negative in the opposite situation, and, zero if the two percentages are equal. The index will most appropriately represent the trichotomy if the middle category is in fact some zero value, as in Table 5–13.

If we assume that one increase and one decrease cancel each other, then the net increase is a good measure of the change for the group as a whole: Skilled manual workers show an increase of 57 per cent and a decrease of 7 per cent—thus a net increase of 50 per cent, the highest among the 11 groups; the armed forces fared worst, with a net decrease of 10 per cent.

TABLE 5–13

Income Changes During the First Year of World War II, 1941–1942*

(per cents in each line representing one occupational group = 100%)

	Per Cent Increase	Per Cent Same	Per Cent Decrease	Net Per Cent Increase†
Major executives	29	53	18	+11
Minor executives (incl. prof.)	40	52	8	+32
All other prof. workers	42	49	9	+33
Salesmen	28	56	16	+12
Clerks (sales & office)	41	49	10	+31
Skilled manual workers	57	36	7	+50
Unskilled workers	45	48	7	+38
Farmers	39	52	9	+30
Farm labor	51	46	3	+48
Not gainfully employed	16	65	19	− 3
Armed forces	34	22	44	−10
Total all groups	40	49	11	+29

* "The Impact of War on American Families," *Life,* April 17, 1943, p. 12. Last column provided by the author.
† Per cent increase minus per cent decrease.

This index, to be sure, has its shortcomings; it does not reflect all variations of the original distribution. Take the following two distributions, both of which yield a balance index of + 10 per cent:

Distribution A	Distribution B
+20%	+50%
=70	=10
−10	−40
100%	100%
(20−10=) +10	(50−40=) +10

Both distributions have the same index but in one the indifferent middle group comprises 70 per cent, in the other only 10 per cent. In Table 5–13, it will be noted, the middle group, with one or two exceptions, happened to fall fairly closely around the 50 per cent figure.[6]

[6] For a discussion of these and other interrelationships, see Paul F. Lazarsfeld and W. S. Robinson, "Some Properties of the Trichotomy 'Like,' 'No Opinion,' 'Dislike,'" *Sociometry,* 1940, p. 151.

SPECIAL SOLUTIONS

It would be a mistake, however, to insist that all reductions of symmetric trichotomies be made in terms of the balance index. Sometimes the subject matter of a table and even the findings one would like to emphasize may suggest a different solution.

In Sam Stouffer's monumental study of the American armed forces during World War II, there is a table that shows the preference of soldiers for northern or southern training camps, depending on whether they themselves were in one or the other, on whether they came originally from the South or the North, and, finally, on whether they were white or Negro. Table 5–14 reproduces the table essentially as it is found in *The American Soldier*.[7]

The table is fairly complex, since it has three pairs of independent variables: origin, race, and region of present camp. The

TABLE 5–14

Soldiers' Preference for Southern or Northern Camp

| | Per Cent Preferring Camp | | | Number of |
	South	Intermediate	North	Soldiers (=100%)
Northern men now in—				
Northern camp				
Negroes	7	18	75	(516)
Whites	11	24	65	(1,470)
Southern Camp				
Negroes	18	19	63	(1,390)
Whites	28	24	48	(1,821)
Southern men now in—				
Northern Camp				
Negroes	31	25	44	(871)
Whites	49	22	29	(360)
Southern Camp				
Negroes	63	23	14	(2,718)
Whites	76	16	8	(1,134)

[7] Sam Stouffer et al., *The American Soldier* (Princeton, N.J.: Princeton University Press, 1949), Vol. 1, p. 554.

temptation, therefore, is great to reduce the trichotomy of the dependent variable in some way. One might choose either the balance index or simply the percentage preferring the northern camp. Table 5–15 gives both.

TABLE 5–15

Soldiers' Preference for Southern or Northern Camp

	Per Cent Preferring Northern Camp	Balance Index (northern preference minus southern preference)
Northern men now in—		
Northern Camp		
Negroes	75	68
Whites	65	54
Southern Camp		
Negroes	63	45
Whites	48	20
Southern men now in—		
Northern Camp		
Negroes	44	13
Whites	29	−20
Southern Camp		
Negroes	14	−49
Whites	8	−68

Since the indeterminate middle group in Table 5–14 is fairly constant, the two rows of figures in Table 5–15 show the same trend, if a different range. But since, unlike the income change in Table 5–13, this table poses major analytical problems, one is inclined to prefer the figure that has a direct psychological meaning, at those preferring the northern camp, rather than at the somewhat more artificial balance index. The table itself is so complicated that one does not want to complicate it more by the use of an index, if the direct—albeit truncated—measure of preference serves the same purpose. Once one has decided for the direct preference percentages, one might go one stage further and consider a variant of the type presented in Table 5–15: not the percentages preferring either North or South, but the percentage preferring *the camp they are in* or the camp they are not in. Table 5–16 is presented in this fashion. It would seem to yield its complicated message more easily than any other version.

TABLE 5–16

Per Cent of Soldiers Preferring the Camp They Are In, by Origin, Race, and Site of Camp

	Northerners		Southerners	
	Negroes	Whites	Negroes	Whites
In northern camp	75	65	44	29
In southern camp	18	28	63	76

While such a table loses some detail, it makes easy reading of several complicated points:

(1) The Negroes in northern camps like the camp they are in better than their white countrymen (75 per cent vs. 65 per cent and 44 per cent vs. 29 per cent); the difference is more marked for the Southerners (44 per cent vs. 29 per cent) than for the Northerners (75 per cent vs. 65 per cent).

(2) In southern camps it is the whites who like it better where they are, irrespective of their origin (28 per cent vs. 18 per cent and 76 per cent vs. 63 per cent).

(3) Northern Negroes in a northern camp are as happy (75 per cent) as southern whites in a southern camp (76 per cent); northern whites in a northern camp are as happy (65 per cent) as southern Negroes in a southern camp (63 per cent) and southern whites are as happy (or unhappy) in the North (29 per cent) as the northern whites in a southern camp (28 per cent).

(4) But Negroes from the South prefer their camp if they are in the North (44 per cent), and the lowest level is reached by the northern Negro based in the South (18 per cent).

SUMMARY

Only tables with not more than two variables can be presented in their entirety and still be clearly readable. Additional variables pose the problem of presenting three or more dimensions in a two-dimensional space. The problem can be solved by telescoping one dimension into a single figure: a percentage, an average, a ratio, or another figure that may be taken to represent the entire column. Just which of these it ought to be depends on the nature of the measure, on the distribution of the numbers in the column, and also on the purpose of the table.

6

INDICES

IN THE preceding chapter we have discussed various ways by which a column of numbers can be represented by one simple figure: an index to stand for the distribution of the column. In this chapter we shall expand the discussion of indices and consider more systematically their variety, their function, and the problems of their construction. In essence, they measure a more-dimensional concept through one single figure; for example, the change in the prices of goods and services by the cost-of-living index; the state of health of a nation by its rate of infant mortality; the beauty of a young lady by the rank given to her by judges in a contest; a student's intelligence by his IQ;[1] and so forth.

The complexity that an index attempts to summarize may refer either to the multitude of units, as in the cost-of-living index, or to the many dimensions of a single unit, as in the beauty contest.

When does one need an index? Whenever one wants to measure or, at least, rank a complex phenomenon; whenever one must decide how to rank performance in a contest or in a class;

[1] To measure psychological and aesthetic concepts was envisioned by Quételet who in 1835 wrote: "Psychological criteria are in this respect . . . not too different from physical properties: one can estimate their magnitude provided that they are in some relationship to the effects which they produce." (*Essai de Physique Sociale*, Bachelier, Paris, 1835, Vol. 2, p. 98.)

whenever one wants to predict which ones among several children promise to be the better students in years to come; whenever one wants to know by how much living expenses have risen so as, for instance, to adjust wages to the change; whenever one wants to know whether the nation's health has improved or deteriorated.

INDEX STRUCTURE

Like houses, indices are constructed by methods of varying durability. For the ranking of participants in a beauty contest, a one-time affair, the index formula may consist of not more than the average score given by the judges. A good[2] cost-of-living index, on the other hand, will require a most elaborate

TABLE 6–1

Schematic Structure of the Cost-of-Living Index

Per Cent Change

	Food	.60 × +2 = +1.20%
Shelter	.25 × −1 = −0.25
Services	.15 × +1 = +0.15
Total	1.10%

[2] The notion of a poor index is discussed on pp. 84f.

sampling of goods and services in a great variety of communities: the price of white bread, chuck steak, chicken, milk, a haircut, having a blouse cleaned, a subway ride, the interest rate on a mortgage. In the end these price changes are combined into subindices for food, shelter, and services and eventually into the over-all cost-of-living index, as outlined in Table 6–1.

The cost-of-living index is thus the weighted average of many prices, the weights being determined by the relative share of the sampled goods in the budgets which they are to reflect.[3]

JUDGMENTS AND MEASUREMENT

The beauty index and the cost-of-living index differ not only in complexity, but also in that the one is based on subjective judgments only, while the other uses, at least in theory, only objectively defined data. The point clearly affects the durability of the index: A price index enables us to compare prices over a long stretch of time, but that Miss X won first rank in last year's beauty contest, while Miss Y reached only second place in this year's contest, does not enable us to say who of the two ladies is the more beautiful: Contest rankings, unlike prices, allow no comparisons over time.

This is why records are kept, for instance, for the Olympic decathlon, and why no meaningful records can be kept for springboard diving. Both performances are scored by complex index formulas, yet only the one is free from subjective judgments.

The participants in a diving contest are scored along two dimensions: the perfection with which each dive is performed, graded by a group of judges in whole integers from 1 (complete failure) to 10 (perfection); their average grade is weighted by the difficulty of the particular dive so that a 7 performance of a difficult dive is worth more than a 7 performance of a sim-

[3] On the intricacies of this index compare *The Price Statistics of the Federal Government* (a report by the Price Statistics Review Committee, George J. Stigler, Chairman), Joint Economic Committee Hearings, U.S. Congress, Jan. 24, 1961.

ple dive. Again, we have measured units and weights, but this time—unlike in the cost-of-living index—neither one is predetermined; both are derived from judgments, although one dimension, the difficulty of the dive, is standardized.

There are altogether 72 basic dives, with variations as to the altitude of the springboard (four heights), as to whether or not the dive began from a running or a standing start, and as to the position of the hands at the beginning of the dive. The degrees of difficulty, that is, the weights accorded to each dive, are standardized judgments of experts. These standard weights range from 1.0 for the simplest dive to 2.9 for the most difficult one. In Table 6–2, the diving score for one hypothetical contestant is developed.

TABLE 6–2

Diving Score for Contestant X

	Performance Score from Three Judges		Grade of Difficulty	Weighted Score
	Individual scores	Average	Standardized	(col. 2 × col. 3)
	(1)	(2)	(3)	(4)
Forward diving from 1m. board, hands tucked	8,9,7	8.00	1.0	8.00
Back dive from 5m. board	5,7,7	6.33	1.6	10.13
Reverse 1 ½ somersault, running from 10m. board, pike position	8,7,8	7.33	2.2	16.13
Forward 1 ½ somersault, 3 twists, from 3m. board	4,6,4	4.67	2.9	13.54
			Total	47.80
		Average (Total/4=)		11.95

Class or school records, although they too are based exclusively on judgments, may nevertheless have validity over time, to the extent that the instructors—the judges—remain the same; in giving a top grade of, say, 95 to a student, the instructor may compare him with a student to whom he gave a 93 some years earlier.

A third variant of index begins with intuitive judgments and ends up in an objective formula. Thus an index of marital happiness was developed[4] by first listing the criteria that characterize successful marriages and are absent in unhappy ones, such as: going out together (rather than separately), observing the wedding anniversary, writing letters if temporarily separated, having mutual friends, and so forth. Or criteria that are present in unhappy marriages and absent in successful ones: angry disputes, separate interests, difficulties of communications, and so forth. These criteria are then formalized and assigned numerical values.[5]

Go out together (rather than separately)	Almost always	+1
	Half and half	0
	Hardly ever	−1
Observe wedding anniversary	Regularly	+1
	Occasionally	0
	Never	−1
How often does husband or wife write or telephone if absent for one week	Two times or more	+1
	Once	0
	Not at all	−1

THE INDEX OBJECT

If the index is built according to a formula, however simple or complicated, there is one sense in which the question of what the index measures cannot arise. The index obviously measures what the formula says it does: the diving score—the quality of the

[4] By Ernest W. Burgess and Leonard S. Cottrell, Jr., *Predicting Success or Failure in Marriage* (Englewood Cliffs, N. J.: Prentice-Hall, 1939).

[5] To be sure, in a minor degree judgment re-enters the process, but its role can be minimized by having several judges or, even better, by replacing imprecise numerals such as "occasionally" or "regularly" by precise ones, as was done with the third item in this example. See Paul F. Lazarsfeld and W. S. Robinson, "The Quantification of Case Studies," *Journal of Applied Psychology*, 1940.

diving performance; the cost-of-living index—the average price change of a representative group of goods and services; the IQ—performance in a number of test situations. As a rule, however, the index measures in addition something *indirectly* related to what it measures directly; often this "something" may be the true index object.

By measuring certain selected goods and services, the cost-of-living index is designed to measure the universe of which the selected items form a sample; the IQ test score is designed to measure the respondent's ability to observe and to reason correctly not only in the test situation but also in future problem situations.

Generally, then, an index will measure whatever object is in some way related to the immediate target of measurement. Thus, the infant mortality rate is taken as an index of the nation's health and is expected to move downward as general health standards improve; the number of windows in a person's home was in former times taken as a rough index of his wealth.[6] Even indices that appear to be designed only for a particular event, such as sport records, can be seen as indicators of related objects—as samples of *future* performances—and thus serve as a basis for selecting, for instance national representation in forthcoming international contests.

LABELS AND CONTENT

The relationship between index formula and object is not always self-evident. Often, an established label for an index will take over and discourage questions necessary to determine its validity. The IQ is such an index. It claims to measure our "intelligence." But how are we to know whether it does or not? The answer can be developed along two lines. One can attempt

[6] For example, the Austrian government during the eighteenth century levied a tax based on the number of windows.

to show that the test questions are so designed that finding the correct answer does not hinge on education or learning, but only on the ability to perceive and reason correctly. Or one can show that the IQ has been highly predictive of future scholastic and other achievements in which intelligence is a prime factor.[7]

Labels, since they consist of words rather than of mathematical symbols, are necessarily vague. Just how ambiguous such labels can be will be seen from Tables 6–3 and 6–4. Both deal with *wage levels*, one comparing them over time, the other, over different areas. Table 6–3 allows *wage level* to be defined in three different ways and, depending on the definition one chooses, the comparison will lead to a different result.

TABLE 6–3

"Wage Levels" in 1919 and 1927[*]

	Hourly Wage Rate		Daily Wage Rate		Annual Earnings	
	1919	1927	1919	1927	1919	1927
Foreman	$1.20	$1.50	$12.00	$12.00	$3,600	$2,880
Skilled operators	0.80	1.00	8.00	8.00	2,400	1,920
Unskilled laborers	0.40	0.50	4.00	4.00	1,200	960

* From Willford I. King, *Index Numbers Elucidated* (New York: 1930), p. 29.

First, "Wage level" can be defined as *average wage rate per hour;* this measure disregards the number of hours actually worked.

Second, "Wage level" can be defined as the *average daily earnings*; this is the product of the hourly wage rate and the average number of hours worked per day. It will vary from index (1)

[7] Questions have been raised concerning the first argument, whether the IQ does not unintentionally measure more than innate ability. Growing up in a well-to-do, educated home, it is argued, may enable a child to perceive better and to reason better. The point for us is not whether this particular proposition is true or false, but rather how it could be proven to be either true or false. Clearly, unless there is a way of measuring innate and learned ability independently by some other method and seeing whether the IQ measures only one or both, the question will remain moot.

only if a change occurred in the number of working hours per day.

And third, "wage level" can be defined as *average annual earnings*; this is the product of the average daily earnings and the number of working days. It measures the workers' total income; and will vary from index (2) only if a change occurred in the number of working days per year.

In the first case, the hourly wage rate increased by 25 per cent (change in dollar value is disregarded in order not to complicate matters more).

In the second case, the daily wage rate remained unchanged, indicating that the increase in hourly rates was offset by a reduction of daily working hours.

In the third case, the annual earnings dropped by 20 per cent because, in addition to a reduction of working hours per day, the number of total working days declined.

To ask which of these indices is the correct one is meaningless. Each is correct in what it measures, and the choice of index must depend on what one wants to measure.

The first index, the hourly wage rate, might be the proper measure of the effectiveness of trade-union activity. The third index is obviously the best measure of the worker's over-all standard of living. The second index is probably the least useful one; to measure daily working hours but to disregard the number of working days is not a very relevant perspective.

Table 6–4 introduces still another element into the wage level concept: the differential wage rate for men and women.

TABLE 6–4

*Comparison of Wages in Two Areas**

Area	Number of Men	Number of Women	Total Workers	Daily Wage For Men	Wage For Women	Average Daily Wage per Worker (regardless of sex)
A	1,000	1,000	2,000	$15.00	$5.00	$10.00
B	1,800	200	2,000	12.00	4.00	11.20

* Adapted from Franz Zizek, *Statistical Averages* (New York: 1913), p. 35.

There are two ways of comparing the wage levels in A and B:

(1) The daily wage rate both for men and women is higher in Area A than in Area B.
(2) The average daily wage per worker is higher in Area B than in Area A.

Both statements are correct. However, in a loosely made statement about the "wage level in A and B," the two statements would seem to contradict each other; but if the statements are made with precision, they are not incompatible.

ACCURACY AND SIMPLICITY

Once an index is seen as indicating a larger, related object, two quality criteria become pertinent: accuracy and simplicity.

By accuracy is meant the precision with which an index measures its object; and simplicity may refer either to the ease with which the necessary data can be collected or to the relative complexity of the index formula. As a rule, accuracy and simplicity compete with each other; the more an index has of the one, the less it usually has of the other.[8]

Some of the more common baseball indices illustrate the point. The best-known measure of a player's hitting ability is his batting average:

$$\text{batting average} = \frac{\text{number of hits}}{\text{times at bat}}$$

The batting average is thus the percentage of successful hits. The percentage is *not* identical with the frequency with which the player got on base; he may get on base not because he had hit

[8] If the data collection amounts only to a sampling problem, then the difficulty of data collection will not compete with the simplicity of the index; a cost-of-living index based on a large and carefully stratified sample is just as "simple" as one that is based on a poor sample.

well, but because the opposing team had made a fielding error; such an instance counts as "at bat" but not as a hit and hence, increases the denominator without increasing the numerator, just as if he had been out on that attempt. Instances in which the player gets on base because of a base on balls or because he was hit by a pitched ball, enter neither the numerator nor the denominator, on the theory that such an event provided no full opportunity for the batting test. For the same reason, the batting average is not affected by a sacrifice hit, where the player is *ordered* to hit into an out—albeit in a certain direction—so as to advance the base runners.

The batting average thus measures a player's batting performance in terms of the dichotomy of either getting a hit or being out.

Even so, the batting average is not a perfect measure of a player's over-all performance; it is not even a perfect measure of his hitting ability, since it does not differentiate between single base hits and extra base hits. That function is performed by the slugging average:

$$\text{slugging average} = \frac{\text{total bases}}{\text{times at bat}}$$

where total bases = $1 \times$ singles $+ 2 \times$ doubles $+ 3 \times$ triples $+ 4 \times$ home runs.

A comparison between the two batting indices is instructive. Table 6–5 presents two examples:

TABLE 6–5

Batting and Slugging Average

	At Bat	Singles	Doubles	Triples	Home Runs	Batting Average	Slugging Average
Player A	500	100	30	10	10	.300	.400
Player B	500	130	10	10	–	.300	.360
Player C	500	80	10	–	20	.220	.360

Players A and B have the same batting average, but A has the higher slugging average; players B and C have the same slugging average, but B has the higher batting average.

Note that the slugging average, because it is a more perfect measure of a batter's hitting ability than the batting average, is in other respects an inferior index. For one thing, there are moments in a baseball game where the crucial question is not "How well will he hit?" but simply "Will he hit or will he be out?" In such situations the batting average is the superior index. The batting average has yet another advantage, namely, it is easily understood. If a player has a batting average of .333 and comes to bat, everybody knows what it means: The odds are 1 in 3 that he will get a hit. The slugging average has no such easily perceivable meaning: there is no simple way of understanding the slugging average, or of projecting it into some simple odds because it is a *combined* measure of *frequency* and *quality* of hitting, measuring the product of both. Hence, there is no way of knowing whether .340 is the result of frequent but relatively poor hitting, or of good but relatively infrequent hitting.[9]

INTERRELATED PERCENTAGES

The following example, from the field of readership research, presents a set of rather simple indices. From three basic sets of field data, percentages are developed that measure important

[9] Even jointly these two indices, the batting and the slugging average, do not cover the total hitting capacity of a player: A sacrifice hit or bunt is not measured by any of these indices. To arrive at the over-all measure of a player's offensive capacity one must then add his ability to run and steal bases. See in this context Earnshaw Cook and Wendell R. Garner, *Percentage Baseball* (Cambridge, Mass.: M.I.T. Press, 1964). For an over-all measure, the authors suggest the "scoring index": the probability (based on past performance) of a player's getting on base, times the probability that he will advance home. This index has the advantage that it permits integration of all players into a team index (*Ibid.*, Chap. 12).

editorial aspects of the items offered in a magazine.[10] A sample of readers of that magazine were asked the following question for each item in the issue:

(A) Did you see this item?
If yes to A: (B) Did you start reading it?
If yes to B: (C) Did you finish reading it?

For each item, here for story MM, a set of figures was thus obtained, as shown in Table 6–6.

TABLE 6–6

Readership of Story MM

		Number of Readers
(*A*)	Saw the item	900
(*B*)	Started reading it	800
(*C*)	Finished reading it	200
(*T*)	Total readers	1,000

There is some overlapping in these answers. The 200 who finished reading the story are part of the 800 who started reading it, and these 800 are in turn part of the 900 who saw the item.

The reason for collecting these data for a magazine was to help the editors in learning how "good" each item in the magazine was, and what reasons accounted for some items being "better" than others. Let us see how we can put our sets of figures to use in solving these two problems.

The first step is to define more precisely the notion of a "good" (or "bad") item. For the editor's over-all purpose, the following definition was acceptable: He would call one item "better" than the other, if it had been read through to the end by more readers than had the other item. The proper combination of two of our figures, therefore, will provide the answer to the

[10] Originally developed for *This Week* magazine. See M. White and H. Zeisel, "Reading Indices," *Journal of Marketing,* October 1941, pp. 103–111.

question "How good was each item?"; namely, the proportion of all readers of the magazine who finished reading the item. In our example the ratio C/T is 2.0.

The next step is to see whether other combinations can be formed from our data that would suggest in a general way why an item was as well or as poorly read as indicated by the ratio C/T.

Obviously, the possibilities are limited, since we have altogether only four figures for each editorial item (A, B, C, and T). But if we can assign meaningful clusters of reasons to the three stages of "reading" which we have measured (seeing—started reading—finished reading), then our problem is solved. The following three indices were developed:

1. Ratio A/T. This is the proportion of readers who noticed the item when paging through the magazine, or more accurately, remembered having seen it. We might take this as a measurement of all factors that account for *attracting the reader's initial attention,* such as position in the magazine, size of the title, layout, size and colors of illustration. For story MM this index is .90.

2. Ratio B/A. This index represents the proportion who started reading the item of those who reported they had noticed it. We will use this as a measure of the *appeal of the subject matter* as suggested by the title, illustration, and similar factors. For story MM this index is .89.

3. Ratio C/B. This index, the proportion of those who finished the item among those who started reading it, is a measure of the item's *holding power,* built up by such factors as attractiveness of content, development of plot, relative length, difficulty of style. For story MM this index is .25.

Note that all these indices have the following uniform mathematical properties: they may vary between 0.00 and 1.00, the latter value expressing the possible optimum, the zero value representing the poorest possible performance.

The usefulness of these indices can be judged best if our story MM is compared with two other stories, as in Table 6–7.

TABLE 6–7

Readership Data for Three Stories

	Story MM	Story NN	Story OO
(A) Saw the item	900	300	800
(B) Started reading it	800	300	200
(C) Finished reading it	200	300	100
(T) Total magazine readers	1,000	1,000	1,000

Table 6–8 shows these data translated into index form.

TABLE 6–8

Reading Indices for Three Stories

	Story MM	Story NN	Story OO
Complete readership (C/T)	.20	.30	.10
Attention value (A/T)	.90	.30	.80
Attractiveness of subject (B/A)	.89	1.00	.25
Holding power (C/B)	.25	1.00	.50

Let us look at the figures in the first line of Table 6–8. They measure the over-all result of the editor's efforts in terms of complete readership. From it we learn that story NN went over best (.30), followed by story MM (.20) and the story OO (.10). The three indices that follow then explain *why* the total readership is as high or low as it is. Story MM, for example, was seen by almost everybody (.90), and almost everybody who saw it started reading it (.89). Clearly, the story's presentation and position in the magazine were such as to attract wide attention. And the subject matter, as suggested by title, illustration, and so on, must have been attractive, since eight out of nine readers who saw the item started reading it. However, for some reasons, the story itself did not hold the readers' interest to the end; for index C/B shows the low value of .25, signaling to the editor that this story's weakness was in the text itself.

Story NN was seen by only a small proportion of the readers (.30); its position and presentation, therefore, must have been relatively poor. However, everybody who saw the item began reading it (1.00), and the development of the story itself lived up to its promise, because the holding power index, too, reaches its top value (1.00); everybody who saw the item finished reading it.

Story OO was seen by many readers (.80), but only a few of them started reading it (.25). Presentation and position must have been good. But the suggested content was unattractive, and only half of those who started to read it finished it (.50).

The next research step that suggested itself was to extend the why question a step further and ask: "What are the precise elements connected with each item that make the attention index high or low? that make a story look attractive or unattractive to the prospective reader? that keep or lose a reader, once he begins reading a story?" These questions can be answered by seeing which characteristics of an item—placement, make-up, size, illustration, style—are related to high or to low values of the three indices.[11]

SOCIOMETRIC INDICES

The indices described on the following pages are based on attitude scores of the type developed by the so-called sociometric school. These scores describe the structure of a small group such

[11] Such an analysis was made by Evelyn Perloff, "Prediction of Male Readership of Magazine Articles," and a parallel paper on female readership, *Journal of Applied Psychology,* 1948, pp. 663–674, and 1949, pp. 175–180. The papers are based on surveys of the Curtis Publishing Company, which found these indices a useful basis for its editorial research operations.

as a class, a Boy Scout troop, or a workshop; each member of the group is asked to state his attitude toward every other member in terms of a simple five-point scale ranging from maximum acceptance $(+1.0)$ to complete rejection (-1.0), with a neutral midpoint (at 0.0) in between.

Table 6–9 presents the mutual attitude scores of a group of seven; $+1$ indicates maximum acceptance, -1 minimum acceptance; $+.5$, 0, and $-.5$ are the three intermediate values. Thus, the 1 on the crossing point III (top) and II (left) means: Member III expressed full acceptance of Member II.

TABLE 6–9

*Interpersonal Attitudes in a Group of Seven**

Received Attitudes by Individual Number	Expressed Attitudes by Individual Number:							Total Score Received
	I	II	III	IV	V	VI	VII	
I	—	1.0	0.0	0.0	0.0	0.5	1.0	2.5
II	1.0	—	1.0	1.0	0.5	0.5	0.5	4.5
III	0.0	0.0	—	0.0	0.0	0.5	0.0	0.5
IV	0.5	0.0	0.5	—	0.5	1.0	0.5	3.0
V	0.5	−1.0	0.0	0.5	—	1.0	0.0	1.0
VI	0.0	0.5	−1.0	−1.0	0.0	—	0.0	−1.5
VII	0.0	0.0	−0.5	0.0	0.5	0.5	—	0.5
Total score given	2.0	0.5	0.0	0.5	1.5	4.0	2.0	

* Taken from Leslie D. Zeleney, "Status: Its Measurement and Control in Education," *Sociometry*, 1941, p. 198.

The analysis of such attitude scores reveals certain group patterns as well as certain characteristics of individual members that can be described effectively with the help of indices.

The first six indices below describe the individuals; Index 7 characterizes the relationship between pairs; and Index 8 characterizes the group as a whole.

Index 1, *mean score received,* indicates the individual's acceptance by the group. It is obtained by dividing the last column of Table 6–9, the total score received, by 6. It may vary, as the individual scores do, between + 1.0 and − 1.0. The indices for each individual are: I (.41), II (.75), III (.08), IV (.50), V (.17), VI (− .25), VII (.08). Acceptance of individual II is highest; VI is least accepted.

Index 2, *average deviation from the mean score received,* indicates the degree of unanimity by which Index 1 was attributed to each individual. A zero deviation means that the same score was attributed to the individual by all six of the other members of the group.

The average amount by which the six individual scores deviate from Index 1 for each of the seven individuals is: I (.42), II (.25), III (.14), IV (.17), V (.50), VI (.50), VII (.25). The group verdict about III is relatively homogeneous (.14); acceptance of V and VI shows relatively the greatest variation from one member of the group to the other (.50).

Index 3, *mean score expressed,* indicates the "active sociability" of the individual, the degree to which he, in turn, accepts the other members in the group. The scores are: I (.33), II (.08), III (0.0), IV (.08), V (.25), VI (.67), VII (.33). Number VI shows the greatest readiness to accept others (.67)—III (0.0) the smallest.

Index 4, *average deviation from the mean score expressed,* shows the degree to which each individual discriminates in his acceptance of other members.

The values are: I (.33), II (.43), III (.50), IV (.43), V (.25), VI (.22), VII (.33). Number VI differentiates least in accepting his colleagues (.22); III shows the greatest degree of differentiation (.50).

Index 5, *a measure of correlation between the scores expressed by the individual towards the other members of the group, and the score he received from each of them,* show the degree to which the individual reciprocates the acceptance accorded to him. Following is the Spearman coefficient of rank correlation[12] for each member of the group: I (.17), II (.43), III (− .19), IV (− .51), V (.17), VI (.17), VII (− .11). Individual II reciprocates most accurately the acceptance he receives from the group (.43). Number IV scores his colleagues pretty much contrary to the acceptance he receives from them (− .51), and for VII one might say that the acceptance he accords is rather independent (− .11) from the one he receives in turn from his colleagues.

Index 6, *a measure of correlation between the scores expressed for each individual and the general mean score (Index 1) of acceptance of each individual,* indicates the degree to which the scores expressed by each individual conform with the general opinion as expressed by the group as a whole.[13] The Spearman coefficient of rank correlation is: I (.94), II (.14), III (1.00), IV (.94), V (.69), VI (.71), VII (.83). Number III scored his colleagues exactly as the group as a whole scored them (1.00); II deviated more than any other member in the entire group (.14). That all the coefficients are positive indicates that the group on the whole agrees in its judgments.

Index 7, *mean of score given and score received between any two individuals,* indicates the affinity between these two. Only one of the $(6 \times 7:2 =)$ 21 pair relationships in the group attained the highest possible mutual score $(+ 1.00)$, namely, numbers I and II. The poorest relationships $(- .25)$ are found in the pairs II–V, III–VI, and III–VII. No worse scores than these appear in the group. The remaining seventeen combinations have scores between zero and $+ .25$.

[12] See p. 94.
[13] Here it becomes particularly apparent that in a small group such as this one, the attitude of one individual may have a disproportionate effect on the mean score; it would be negligible if the group were large.

Index 8, *mean of all scores,* indicates the general level of cohesion in the group. With the aid of this index different groups may be compared with respect to their level of cohesion, and changes within the group may be measured over a period of time. The mean of all scores given (and received) in the group is .37. Considering that the hypothetical maximum score is 1.00 (if all scores expressed full acceptance), and the minimum score − 1.00 (if all expressed full rejection) one would probably call this one a moderately cohesive group. A more realistic appraisal of the mean value of .37 would have to come from comparisons with other groups.

THE SPEARMAN COEFFICIENT OF RANK CORRELATION

We now embark on what may seem a gratuitous enterprise, the effort to construct an index that has long been in existence and can be found in any elementary statistics text: the Spearman coefficient of rank correlation. To pretend that we have to invent it should prove to be an instructive exercise.

The problem is to measure the degree of similarity or dissimilarity between any pair of rank orders, each containing the same number of items, as in Table 6–10.

TABLE 6–10

Ranking of Five Contestants by Three Judges

Judge A	Judge B	Judge C
1	2	3
2	1	2
3	3	1
4	5	5
5	4	4

Without much computation it can be seen that Judge A is closer to Judge B than he is to Judge C, but it is not immediately clear whether Judge B is closer to Judge A or to Judge C. It is one of the purposes of an index to provide a measurement sufficiently accurate to distinguish such close comparisons.

How are we to start the development of a similarity index between any two such rank orders? We will properly begin again by defining the two limits which our index may acquire—complete similarity and the exact opposite. In Table 6–11 let us write down these two extremes for a scale of five items, as we used it in our example.

TABLE 6–11

Rank Correlation of Five Items

	Complete Similarity			Exact Opposite	
(a)	(b)	(a × b)	(a)	(b)	(a × b)
1	1	1	1	5	5
2	2	4	2	4	8
3	3	9	3	3	9
4	4	16	4	2	8
5	5	25	5	1	5
		55			35

These two pairs of rank orders have a mathematical property that holds true for scales of any size: The sum of the products of each pair of rank orders reaches a maximum for "complete similarity," and a minimum for the "exact opposite." If the multiplications and additions are carried out, the sum of the products for complete similarity is 55, the sum of the products for exact opposite is 35. The difference between these two extreme values is 20. The product-sums of all other possible combinations of five-item scales lie somewhere between 35 and 55.

These limits, of course, will vary with the length of the scale; for a four-item scale they are 20 and 30; for a six-item scale, 56 and 91, and so forth. Since we would like to build our index formula so that it can be applied to scales of *any* size, it will be advisable to construct it so that the maximum value, that is, complete similarity, always yields an index of + 1.0, and the "exact opposite" always yields an index of − 1.0. The mean product-sum, 45 for the five-item scale, 25 for the four-item scale, and 73.5 for the six-item scale, should always equal 0.0 and represent the midpoint of the index range, as shown in Table 6–12.

The rest develops simply: the distance between − 1.0 and + 1.0 is divided proportionately according to the two limit values:

TABLE 6–12

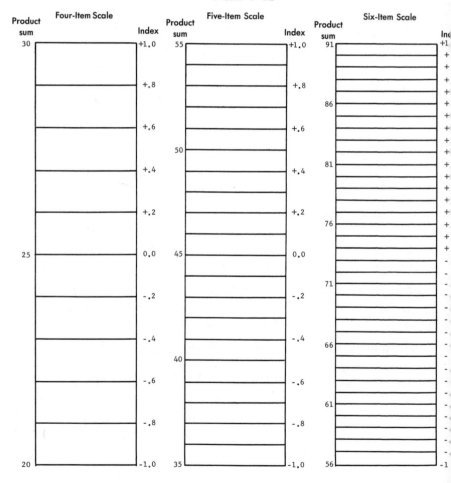

If 35 corresponds to − 1.0, and 55 to + 1.0, then 36 = − .9, 37 is − .8, ... 46 is + .1, 47 is + .2, ... 54 = + .9. For the four-item scale 21 is − .8, 22 is − .6, ... 25 is 0.0, 26 is + .2, etc. For the six-item scale we run into fractions because the distance from − 1.0 to 0.0 equals 17.5 points, but the principle remains the same.

These index values are in fact but the respective values for the Spearman coefficient of rank correlation. It is, of course, much simpler to derive them through the Spearman formula, the more elegant equivalent of our cumbersome but instructive derivation:[14]

$$\rho = 1 - \frac{6 \Sigma D^2}{N \cdot (N^2 - 1)}$$

Σ (sigma) stands for "the sum of," D for the difference between the two ranks given to any one item; and N for the number of items in the scale.

There remains the task of applying the mathematics to our example of the five contestants ranked differently by the three judges. Table 6–13 gives the ρ's, the coefficients of rank correlation for the three pairs of judges:

TABLE 6–13

Rank Correlation Between Three Judges

Judges	Coefficient of Correlation
A and B	+ .8
A and C	+ .5
B and C	+ .6

The views of judges A and B turn out to be closest (+ .8); judges A and C are farthest apart (+ .5); the relationship between judges B and C falls in between (+ .6).

[14] Its mathematical development can be found, for instance, in Charles C. Peters and W. R. Van Voorhis, *Statistical Procedures and Their Mathematical Bases* (New York: 1940), pp. 103–106.

DEVELOPING A COMPLEX INDEX FORMULA

Up to now our examples featured index formulas of relatively simple structure or, if they were complex, they were well-known standard formulas such as the coefficient of correlation. At times, however, the problem at hand demands a specially constructed, custom-made index.

Our example concerns an effort to measure the degree of monopolization of the major media of communications, newspapers and broadcasting stations, in any given community. The question came up in the course of a legal dispute involving radio stations and newspaper publishers before the Federal Communications Commission. The Bureau of Applied Social Research at Columbia University was asked to develop an index measuring the degree of monopolization of the means of public communications. The index was designed to measure the degree to which communications units in one community were concentrated under joint ownership. The following data were used for its construction:

(1) The number of communication units, broadcasting stations and newspapers, in the community.

(2) The extent to which these units were connected through common ownership.

Thus, one would know about a certain community that it had, for instance, two newspapers and two broadcasting stations, and that one newspaper and one of the stations were under joint ownership.

To develop the index formula a number of conditions were set forth, partly derived from the concept of monopolization, and partly from certain formal requirements that would make the index clear and practicable.

(1) No distinction is made between broadcasting stations and newspapers. For purposes of the index each is reduced to the common denominator of "one communication unit."

(2) The index is to vary between 0.0, if there is no joint ownership between competing units (no monopolization) and 1.0 if all units in the community are under joint ownership (complete monopoly).

(3) The index is to grow as the number of competing units decreases: 0-0, 0-0 should have a higher value than 0-0, 0, 0.

(4) The number of competing units being equal, the index is to be higher the more unequal the competing units are: 0-0-0, 0 should produce a higher value than 0-0, 0-0.

The formula finally developed[15] was:

$$I = \frac{\sqrt{X_1^2 + X_2^2 + \ldots + X_n^2}}{N}$$

N stands for the total number of units (newspapers and/or stations) in the community. $X_1, X_2, \ldots, X_n$ stand for the number of units in each joint ownership group. X stands for 2 if two units are under one joint ownership, for 3 if three units are under joint ownership, and so forth; n is the total number of joint ownerships. Single ownership units are not entered into the numerator; hence, if all units are under separate ownership, the numerator, and therefore the index, equals zero.

The formula establishes first the ratio of joint-ownership units to the total number of units, but gives the former in terms of the square root of the sum of the squares to insure that the constellation 0-0-0,0 has a higher value than the combination 0-0,0-0, although both communities have two competing groups.

[15] By Paul Zilsel in cooperation with the author.

By this formula the five possibilities of joint ownership of four units, for example, will be assigned the following index values: (i) 0-0-0-0: $\sqrt{4^2}/4 = 1.00$ (complete monopolization); (ii) 0-0-0,0: $\sqrt{3^2}/4 = .75$; (iii) 0-0,0-0: $\sqrt{2^2 + 2^2}/4 = .71$; (iv) 0-0,0,0: $\sqrt{2^2}/4 = .50$; (v) 0,0,0,0: $\sqrt{0}/4 = 0.00$ (perfect competition).[16]

HOW TO BUILD AN INDEX

Index construction, then, consists, in essence, of three steps: (1) determining the object one wants to measure, (2) putting this measure into operable terms, and (3) implementing these terms with actual data. For example:

> An editor wants to measure (1) how well the various pieces in his magazine catch and hold the reader's interest. Translated into operational terms (2) this means he wants to know for each piece the percentage of readers who start reading the item and finish reading it, once they have begun. He then makes a survey among a sample of his readers (3) in which each is asked, as the interviewer moves from one item in the magazine to the next, (a) whether he had noticed it; (b) whether he had started to read it, (c) whether he had finished reading it. The ratios $a/total$, b/a, and c/b provide the desired measures.[17]

> An investigator wants to test the widely held notions that (1) the citizens of some communities are more claim-conscious than those in other communities; that is, that they are more likely to try to make money out of an accident. Operationally, (2) this would mean more claims per 100 comparable accidents in one city than

[16] For the discussion of two sophisticated indices, designed to measure concentration in *any* industry and their validation either through an underlying theory or empirical correlates see the *Yale Law Journal*, 1967: M. O. Finkelstein and R. O. Friedberg, "The Application of an Entropy Theory of Concentration to the Clayton Act" (p. 677) and the note by George J. Stigler (p. 718).

[17] See p. 87.

in another. Liability insurance companies have data that allow such comparisons (3).[18]

A political scientist wants to develop a measure of voting along class lines: (1) workers voting for the labor party, nonworkers against it. Operationally, (2) if all workers vote labor, and all nonworkers antilabor, the measure ought to reach its maximum, and vice versa. An index of class voting is established: the percentage of workers voting for labor minus the percentage of nonworkers who vote labor. The necessary data (3) are produced through an election poll.[19]

A psychologist wants to measure intelligence (1); he plans to develop four test questions; those who solve all four get the highest rank, those answering only three correctly the next highest, and those answering none, the lowest (2); he then devises four questions of about equal difficulty that require for their solution not learning, but only the ability to reason (3).[20]

SUMMARY

The problem of index construction in its most general form is how to devise a one-dimensional measurement of a more-dimensional object. This is achieved either by having one of the dimensions represent the total, or by an index formula that combines two or more dimensions into one figure. The index formula may consist of ranking judgments, of measurements, or of a combination of both. In one sense, the question as to what an index measures is a tautological one: The formula gives the answer and, in simple situations, that answer will suffice. But in more complex situations, that question goes to the relationship between the directly measured object (e.g., some test questions)

[18] See chapter "Claims Consciousness" in Hans Zeisel et al., *Delay in the Court* (Boston: Little, Brown and Co., 1959).
[19] Note that this index can also be used for measuring the vote along other lines, such as race or religion.
[20] This, in principle, is the method of the IQ measure.

and the ultimate object (e.g., intelligence), as in the IQ, the intelligent quotient. Index formulas vary a great deal, but one of the more prevalent forms is the average, either simple or weighted, as exemplified by price indices. The most interesting applications arise when an index has to be custom-designed. The general problem of index construction is to balance accuracy with simplicity, the latter being in turn related to questions of economy.

PART II

THE SEARCH FOR CAUSES

7

The Tools of Causal Analysis

Most of the work in the social sciences is still directed toward the description of what is and what happens, because there are so many areas of social behavior we have not yet observed with any precision. But more and more frequently, we are trying to find out why things happen and what effects they have. In fact, no other achievement has marked so significantly the progress of the social sciences as the improvement of our ability to explain why people behave the way they do.

Description and causal analysis are seldom sharply separated. Nevertheless, the tools of causal analysis form a rather distinct set. This introductory chapter aims to provide a synopsis of these tools.

THE CONTROLLED EXPERIMENT

The most glamorous tool, because it is the most precise one, we inherited from the natural sciences: the controlled experiment. In its simplest form it begins with a group of people with whom the experiment is to be performed. That group is divided randomly, that is, by some lottery process, into two smaller groups that are for all practical purposes interchangeable *because* they were obtained through random division. One group is then exposed to the experimental influence, while the other is not. This arrangement allows us to ascribe to the experimental influence any effect that appears in the exposed group and not in the other, the control group. In the natural sciences, this is the classic experimental design for measuring, for instance, the effect of a vaccine (Chart 7–1).

CHART 7–1

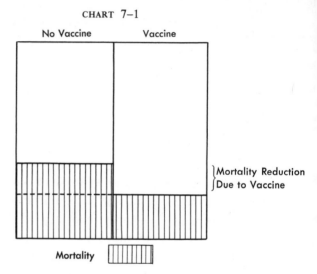

We shall skip here the technical niceties of experimental design. They can be found in any number of texts.[1] Suffice it to say here that the experimental method has the advantage of allowing for the application of what has been called the artichoke principle;[2] that is, it can proceed step by step in disentangling a complex causal problem. Two of the simplest devices for the stepwise treatment of causal problems are: (1) varying one or a few of

[1] For example, D. R. Cox, *Planning of Experiments* (New York: Wiley, 1958); also K. A. Brownlee, "The Principles of Experimental Design," *Industrial Quality Control,* 1957, pp. 1–9. See also S. A. Stouffer, "Some Observations on Study Design," *American Journal of Sociology,* 1949–50, pp. 355–361.

[2] Herman Wold, "Causal Inference from Observational Data," *Journal of the Royal Statistical Society,* 1956, pp. 28–60.

the controlled causal factors at a time, keeping the other ones constant; (2) arranging for additive and linear effects of the controlled variables.

Two remarks are in order concerning peculiar difficulties of experimenting in the social sciences. One concerns the obvious difficulty of experimenting with human beings. It is not by accident that some of the first of these experiments were conducted in the army where one company could be ordered to watch an indoctrination film, while another was used as a control group.[3] Only school classes, hospitals and, of course, prisons, allow similar tight arrangements by the experimenter, and that is why the directly controlled experiment has its limits in social research.

The second remark goes to the scientific yield of experiments in the social sciences. Even if feasible and even if technically precise, the insights they provide are necessarily of a limited nature. That one indoctrination film produces a measurable effect allows little generalization; the next film might be poor and show no effect. Or, to take an example from another field: That a different instruction from the judge to the jury on the law of insanity in a case of housebreaking produces different jury verdicts does not mean that it will also produce different verdicts if the case is murder.[4] The problem of generalizing exists also in the natural sciences, but since they have a more developed structure, wider generalizations are possible and *experimenta crucis,* crucial experiments that allow broad generalizations, can be designed. For the most part, the social sciences as yet lack such a coherent structure and hence such opportunities for broad generalizations.

[3] Carl I. Hovland, Arthur A. Lumsdaine, and Fred D. Sheffield, *Experiments on Mass Communication,* Vol. III of *Studies in Social Psychology in World War II* (Princeton, N. J.: Princeton University Press, 1949).

[4] See Rita James Simon, *The Jury and the Defense of Insanity* (Boston: Little, Brown, 1967).

THE SURVEY CROSS-TABULATION

We began this discussion with the controlled experiment not only because it is in a way the perfect analytical instrument, but also because some of the less powerful tools of analysis are shaped after it.

On the surface, the survey cross-tabulation is indistinguishable from the tabulation of an experiment. It too compares those exposed to the potential cause with those who have not been exposed, but the comparison is made retrospectively, that is, without prior randomization of the two groups, and that makes a big difference. Without prior randomization there is no way of categorically stating that prior to the experimental exposure, the two groups had been interchangeable—an indispensable requirement for ascribing the resulting effect with certainty to the exposure. The survey cross-tabulation is therefore in need of reassurance that in spite of the lack of prior randomization, the two groups had been originally interchangeable.

There is an old Chinese statistical joke to the effect that the people who are visited by a doctor have a considerably higher mortality rate than those who have been spared such a visit. Extreme examples have the advantage of clarifying both the problem and its solution. Obviously, what is needed here is to make the *visit–no visit* comparison separately for those who prior to the event had been sick and those who had not been sick; we would then quickly find out that the latter group could safely be eliminated altogether, because it had no professional visits from doctors. The general prescription here is to split the cross-tabulation into segments and make the exposure–nonexposure comparison separately for each of the subgroups of the total population. And the question now is, along what lines these subgroups should be formed. Again, the doctor example shows the way: We must group the people in such a way that we remove whatever impeded their interchangeability prior to the exposure. Our difficulty was that practically all people in the group who had a doctor visit must have been sick, while those who had no doctor visit probably included some sick persons but also all those who had no need for a doctor. By making the comparison separately for the sick and the healthy, we remove the biasing inequality in the original group. Incidentally, not every inequality will bias the result. If one group in the doctor example had contained more redheads than the other, such inequality would in all probability not have mattered. But if one group had been older than the other, it would have, because older people will, on the whole, die sooner than younger ones.

The trouble with this procedure of fractioned analysis is that however far it is carried, it never guarantees cure; there is no way of knowing for certain that all the hidden factors that will render a causal inference spurious have been eliminated, however plausible the result. This is why statistical confidence tests may be applied to survey data only with discretion.[5] Ultimately, what Michael Polanyi has called personal knowledge must here play an important role.[6] But it would be a mistake to conclude from these analytical difficulties that the survey is generally inferior to the experiment. For one, survey data are gathered in their natural settings where they have developed normally without interference on the part of the manipulating scientist.[7] Secondly, it provides greater opportunities for interlocking the

[5] See Hans Zeisel, "The Significance of Insignificance Differences," *Public Opinion Quarterly*, 1955, Vol. 19, p. 319.

[6] *Personal Knowledge* (London: Routledge & Kegan Paul, Ltd., 1958).

[7] In the study of animal behavior a similar dichotomy exists: The laboratory experiment is but one of its research tools. Systematic observation of animals in their natural settings, sometimes aided by the observer's experimental design, a method developed primarily by Konrad Lorenz and Nikolaas Tinbergen, has emerged as a most powerful research procedure.

variety of relationships, because the scope of the survey is less limited; it permits the testing of hypotheses that were not articulate at the outset, but developed in the process of analyzing the data.

MATCHING

Another method of providing a control group retrospectively is to match those individuals who developed a certain effect with counterparts who, under the same circumstances, failed to develop the particular effect. By comparing the two groups, not with respect to the effect but with respect to the *antecedents* of the effect, causes may be discerned. In a most elegant inquiry, designed to discover the causes of automobile accidents fatal to pedestrians, autopsies were performed on some 50 pedestrians 18 years and over, killed seriatim in Manhattan at known sites and times. The control group was obtained by visiting the accident site on a subsequent date, but on the same day of the week and hour of the day. Interviews and breath specimens for alcohol analysis were obtained from the first four adult pedestrians reaching the site who were of the same sex as the deceased. This highly original study showed that the killed pedestrians came primarily from two high-risk groups: middle-aged persons who drank and old people.[8]

THE NATURAL EXPERIMENT

In rare cases we are almost certain that retrospective data have the quality of a controlled experiment. Consider the following example. It was found that the accident rates of female automobile drivers rise sharply during the days immediately

[8] W. Haddon, Jr., et al., "A Controlled Investigation of the Characteristics of Adult Pedestrians Fatally Injured by Motor Vehicles in Manhattan." *Accident Research*, W. Haddon, E. Suchman, and D. Klein, eds. (New York: Harper & Row, 1964), pp. 232–250.

prior to and following menstruation, and interestingly enough, not so much during the period itself. Since it is highly improbable that women drive during these days more frequently or in more hazardous surroundings, we are allowed to assume that nature has provided us here with a controlled experiment.[9]

A famous natural experimental situation is offered by identical twins: Observation of what in later life they have in common and what separates them allows separating the influences of heredity from influences of milieu.

REASON ANALYSIS

We now come to an entirely different tool of causal research, although we shall eventually connect it with the controlled experiment: the interrogation of the actor as to the motives of his actions. The method is colloquially known as "the art of asking why,"[10] more technically, as reason analysis. The process is complicated, and its success is limited by two facts: Actions are usually the result of a very great number of different causes and motivations; and many of these motives operate unconsciously and are, therefore, difficult to find. The technique, therefore, works best with respect to actions that are relatively simple and that have been taken with some deliberation. Again, an extreme example will be helpful. If a woman is asked why she switched dry cleaners and she answers "The old one ruined two of my dresses," the answer will have the ring of completeness and truth. Even inquiries into more complex consumption decisions, such as "Why did you buy this Buick Special?" or "Why did you go to the Bergman movie last night?" will yield satisfactory answers if the interviewer knows his job. But the more personally

[9] Katherina Dalton, "Menstruation and Accidents" in *ibid.*
[10] From Paul F. Lazarsfeld's pioneering paper of that title (1935), reprinted in D. Katz, et al., *Public Opinion and Propaganda* (New York: Holt, Rinehart and Winston, Inc., 1954).

momentous a decision becomes, the smaller will be the yield from asking why: "Why did you vote Democrat?" is already a much more difficult interviewing subject; and the question "Why did you marry Jean?" is almost bound to be a failure.

REASON ASSESSMENT

There is a variant of reason analysis which it is advisable to consider separately. It has the same aim—namely, to discover the structure of an individual decision process or an individual chain of events—but it does it without questioning the actor. This method is applied, for instance, to automobile or airplane accidents, where the actors are often no longer available for questioning or, at best, conscious of only part of the total chain of circumstances.

By collecting and collating all relevant clues, the analyst, who in this case must be an expert in the particular field, is often able to reconstruct the course of events and assign the cause or causes of the particular incident.

A variant of this method was used in the study designed to find out what reasons led the jury to render, occasionally, a verdict with which the presiding judge disagreed. Here, the judge was the expert who made the assessment, often of course after having discussed the matter with the jury.[11]

In Chapter 12 we will show how cross-tabulation and reason analysis or reason assessment are systematically linked.

MOTIVATION RESEARCH

The advent of psychoanalysis has tempted social scientists into efforts to supplement reason analysis by devices that try to penetrate at least the upper layers of unconscious motivations: tests designed to reveal personality characteristics or

---

[11] See Kalven and Zeisel, *The American Jury* (Boston: Little, Brown, 1967), especially Chapter 7, "The Logic of Explanation."

specific unconscious attitudes. Again, the tool is the interview, but the aim is not the reconstruction of a more or less conscious decision but the discovery of layers of subconscious motivations. The direct question "why?" fails here, because the respondent himself, by definition, does not know his reasons, even if accorded all the patience and help of a good interviewer. This approach has acquired the label "motivation research."

Sometimes the approach is limited to or aided by standardized tests such as the Minnesota Multiphase Personality Inventory or the Rorschach test. More often it is a test developed for the specific purpose that asks the interviewee to answer a set of attitude questions or to draw "a picture" as best as he can of a specified object. The usefulness of all such efforts is predicated on the analyst's ability to establish a meaningful connection between the revealed attitudes and the behavior that is to be explained.[12]

THE INDIRECT EXPERIMENT

We now turn to a type of experiment that has developed in response to the many obstacles that hamper directly controlled experimentation with human beings or social institutions.[13] This type of experiment provides proper random selection of experi-

[12] For the theory, see Paul F. Lazarsfeld, "Progress and Fad in Motivation Research," *Proceedings of the Third Annual Seminar on Social Science for Industry Motivation,* Stanford Research Institute, 1955, pp. 11–23. As to the praxis, see Herta Herzog's classic in Hadley Cantril, Herta Herzog, and H. Gaudet, *The Invasion from Mars—A Study in the Psychology of Panic* (Princeton, N. J.: Princeton University Press, 1940). See also Ernest Dichter, *Handbook of Consumer Motivation* (New York: McGraw-Hill, 1964); James V. McNeal (ed.), *Dimensions of Consumer Behavior* (New York: Appleton-Century-Crofts, 1965); Joseph Newman (ed.), *Unknowing the Consumer* (New York: Wiley, 1966); Karen A. Machover, *Personality Projection in the Drawing of the Human Figure* (Springfield, Ill.: Charles C. Thomas, Publisher, 1949).

[13] Irwin M. Towers, Leo A. Goodman, Hans Zeisel, "A Method of Measuring the Effects of Television Through Controlled Field Experiments," *Studies in Public Communication,* University of Chicago, No. 4, 1962, pp. 87–110.

mental and control groups, but gives up control over the exact degree of exposure. As a result, only part of the experimental group is exposed to the experimental influence, and it is at the outset uncertain how large that part will be. An example will help.

It is one of the major concerns of our civil courts to find out whether *pretrial,* the informal get-together of the litigants and the judge prior to trial, increases the settlement ratio, the proportion of cases that are settled before they come to trial. The ideal way of testing this issue experimentally would have been to pretry one random half of the cases, and forego pretrial with the other half. Concerns over the constitutionality of such discrimination led to the following change in design: instead of foregoing pretrial completely, the cases in the control group were pretried only if one of the litigants demanded it. The success of the design is therefore not secured; it would fail if all the litigants in the experimental group were to demand a pretrial. As it happens, only about half of them demanded it, and a magnificently clear result evolved: obligatory pretrial did nothing to increase or advance settlement.[14]

We might consider one other, albeit hypothetical, example. An indirect experiment could yield final proof of the smoking-cancer hypothesis. The objection to the so far available evidence is that the people who smoke and have a higher cancer rate might have such a higher rate not because they smoke but because of another, probably hidden, factor that causes both smoking and cancer. Yet a direct experiment in which one group is ordered to smoke and another forbidden to smoke is clearly impossible; not even in a prison population could it be enforced.

But an indirect experiment could work. Suppose we took two random groups of smokers and then tried to persuade one group

[14] M. Rosenberg, *The Pretrial Conference and Effective Justice* (New York: Columbia University Press, 1964).

to reduce smoking or give it up altogether. It would not matter how we achieved it; we might persuade them, but we could also bribe them, pay them for not smoking.

If we were at all successful in reducing smoking in the experimental group, a subsequent differential incidence of cancer could then safely be attributed to the reduction in smoking, since this was the only difference between the two groups.

The foregoing examples make clear what distinguishes the indirect from the directly controlled experiment. It abandons direct control over the experimental variable and thereby risks failure if the indirect control fails to create different degrees of exposure. Also, it blunts the measuring situation, because it is not possible any longer to measure directly the effect of the experimental variable. But we gain, in exchange, a feasible experiment where the alternative would have been—no experiment at all. Thus the indirect experiment is merely a special application of the important rule for research in the social sciences, that half a loaf is better than none.

DEVIATION FROM PREDICTION

Still another device for circumventing the obstacles of experimentation must be mentioned. To be sure, it is but a special case of refining retrospective cross-tabulations, but it has important features of its own. The British Home Office, for example, was eager to learn whether certain methods of parole supervision of ex-convicts would reduce the rate of recidivism. Since it seemed inopportune or impossible to make a controlled experiment, the following method was used. There is considerable knowledge from prior studies on the differential rates of parole success for different types of ex-convicts. Thus it was found that family ties, work habits, extent of criminal record, and other factors, in various combinations, were good predictors of the differential success rate. The rationale of the parole supervision study utilized this prediction by comparing not the crude success rate in the experimental and control group, but rather the *deviation* of the crude success rate from the rate predicted for these individuals by the prediction formula. The difference between the predicted and the actual (crude) success rate was then ascribed to the treatment.

THE PANEL TECHNIQUE

For certain problems, the traditional survey technique, which assembled all data at the same time in one interview, proved clearly insufficient. If one wanted to find out whether a certain factor could have caused a certain effect, one would like to be sure at least that the cause preceded the effect in time. If it did not, it could not have been its cause. The reconstruction of this sequence in one interview is often impossible. For example, if one coordinates advertising expenditures and profits for any group of corporations, they will invariably show a positive correlation: High advertising expenditures go with high profits and vice versa. But to prove the implication that advertising contributed to the higher profits it is necessary to show that a change in the advertising expenditure *preceded* the change in the profit picture; it could have happened, and often does happen, of course, that the advertising expenditure was increased because business was good and profits were high.

To resolve this and a host of other difficulties, the panel technique was developed: the interviewing of the same respondent repeatedly, at intervals. Not that it constitutes by itself a special mode of causal analysis. Rather its usefulness may be compared to that of a ladder that facilitates access to more, and more orderly, data. Its essence is that it allows us several observations of the same unit—of a person, a family, or a store—over time. Its major methodological advantage is that it enables us to learn the sequence of events, and thereby to facilitate the identification of cause and effect. In addition, the panel has the advantage of allowing us to collect much more information about any one unit than the one-shot survey can provide. The panel may also be used as a vehicle for controlled experimentation.[15]

At this point the ring closes and we arrive where we have started—at the controlled experiment, which by definition requires at least one before- and one after-observation of the experimental and the control unit.

The following chapters do not deal with all these approaches to causal analysis; perhaps they will in some future edition. For the time being they deal with three areas: the survey cross-tabulation (Chapters 8 and 9); reason analysis (Chapters 10 and 11); and the panel technique (Chapter 13). Chapter 12 deals with the confluence of proof from different sources.

SUMMARY

The methods of probing into causal relationships within the realm of the social sciences have developed partly in analogy to the natural sciences. Partly, however, they represent indigenous developments born out of the special limitations and opportunities that research on human motivations offers. The controlled experiment is the most precise tool, but few situations allow its application. Even so, the controlled experiment serves as paradigm for most other research approaches, each of which simulates it in some respect, although never completely. The most frequent simulation of the controlled experiment is the survey cross-tabulation, which lacks the all-important step of randomization prior to the separation of experimental and control group. Reason analysis and the other approaches that rely on analyzing the individual act are in a specifiable form related to experimental and quasi-experimental methods. The remainder of the book discusses some of the tools of causal analysis in detail.

[15] Towers, Goodman, Zeisel, *op. cit.*

8

THE CROSS-TABULATION REFINES

THE STARTING point of any statistical analysis is the one-dimensional, straightforward table, showing a distribution among several groups, in its simplest form, among two groups as in Table 8–1.[1] From this simplest of all statistical tables, one can learn that at the time of the poll there was a bare majority for the Republican candidate, and that if things did not change, the Republican candidate could expect to carry the county. Thus, such a straight table has descriptive and to some extent predictive value.

PURPOSE OF CROSS-TABULATION

Looked at in another way, such a table is but the starting point for explorations that proceed by dividing the sample into subgroups, in order to learn how the dependent variable (voting Republican or Democrat, in this case) varies from one group to the other. This, then, is the function of the cross-tabulation.

If the new, two-dimensional distribution differs from the old one-dimensional one, one step has been taken in the process

[1] This table and the ones that follow are adaptations from a study of the Willkie-Roosevelt presidential campaign of 1940, as mirrored in a small Ohio town. That pioneering study was later published in Paul F. Lazarsfeld, Hazel Gaudet, and Bernard Berelson, *The People's Choice* (New York: Columbia University Press, 1948). See also Tables 13–17 ff.

TABLE 8–1

Sample Poll in County X Before Presidential Election

Will Vote For	Per Cent
Republican candidate	52
Democratic candidate	48
Total	100
(Number of cases)	(5,160)

of discovering the factors that determine the over-all proportions. For example, if the table is broken down by the prospective voter's economic status, Table 8–2 is obtained:

TABLE 8–2

Preelection Poll in County X by Economic Status

	Economic Status	
	High	Low
	%	%
Republican	60	45
Democrat	40	55
Total	100	100
(Number of cases)	(2,604)	(2,556)

This table shows that the proportion of Republican voters is larger among voters from the upper economic strata than from the lower. Conversely, the proportion of Democratic voters is larger in the lower economic brackets. Thus, generally speaking, economic status is one factor that determines the proportion of Democratic and Republican votes.

Such a fourfold, or two-by-two, table is the simplest type of cross-tabulation. Its purpose, as that of any cross-tabulation, is to find out whether the proportions to be studied vary significantly in the two (or more) subgroups of the sample.

Table 8–3 is another example from one of the many studies of automobile accidents.

If we want to find out what factors characterize the people who have automobile accidents, we must begin by finding sub-

TABLE 8–3

*Accident Rate of Automobile Drivers**

	Per Cent
Never had an accident while driving	62
Had at least one accident while driving	38
Total	100
(Number of cases)	(14,030)

* The example is based on poll data of the American Institute of Public Opinion, as reproduced in *Smash Hits of the Year* (The Travelers Insurance Co., Hartford, 1940). Only the proportion of accidents is actually taken from these data; the remaining data presented here are fictitious.

groups which we suspect of having many accidents, and other groups which have relatively few. If we suspect, for instance, that the driver's sex affects the accident rate, we would break the sample down into male and female drivers, as in Table 8–4.

TABLE 8–4

Accident Rate of Male and Female Drivers

	Men	Women
	%	%
Never had an accident while driving	56	68
Had at least one accident while driving	44	32
Total	100	100
(Number of cases)	(7,080)	(6,950)

This table sustains the hunch that a larger proportion of male drivers have accidents than female drivers. By having introduced the additional factor (sex) into the analysis, the preliminary result is refined and light is shed on the factors that determine the original distribution.

TYPES OF CROSS-TABULATION

The procedure can be extended, of course, by injecting alternate factors into the tabulation. Such a series of *alternative* breakdowns—by sex, by age, by economic status, and so on—are the prevalent form in which statistical surveys are presented. Yet, as the following paragraphs show, the results of such alternative cross-tabulations by various factors are unsatisfactory and sometimes even misleading. The correct procedure is to introduce each additional factor not as an alternative to, but simultaneously with, the other factors so that all possible interrelations among these factors become visible.

The simultaneous introduction of additional factors may produce any of the following effects:

1. It may *refine* the results of the simple cross-tabulation.
2. It may fail to refine the results of the simple cross-tabulation but may reveal an *independent* effect of a third factor.
3. It may *explain* the results of the simple cross-tabulation:
   a. by *confirming* the original interpretation
   b. by *revealing* the original interpretation as *spurious.*

After discussing these three types of relationships in Chapters 8 and 9, we shall discuss, at the end of Chapter 9, certain practical applications of these insights to the routine of research work.

THE ADDITIONAL FACTOR REFINES THE CORRELATION

By a simple cross-tabulation, users of a certain type of breakfast food were found to be more frequent among people below forty years than among older ones (Table 8–5).

TABLE 8–5

Use of Breakfast Food XX, by Age

	Below 40	40 and Over
	%	%
Use XX	28	20
Don't use XX	72	80
Total	100	100
(Number of cases)	(1,224)	(952)

The investigator thought of sex as an additional factor influencing the use of XX breakfast food. The proper way of introducing this new factor into the analysis is shown by the scheme in Table 8–6. To simplify the table, the percentage of those who do *not* use XX were omitted:

TABLE 8–6

Use of Breakfast Food XX, by Sex and Age

	Men		Women	
	Below 40	40 and Over	Below 40	40 and Over
Eat XX	36%	23%	20%	17%
(Number of cases)	(619)	(480)	(605)	(472)

This table presents the relationship between age and use of XX under two different conditions: one for men and one for women. Table 8–5 showed that a relationship exists between age and the use of XX. Table 8–6 now refines this knowledge by showing how this age relationship differs for the two sexes: age differentiates more sharply among men (36 per cent versus 23 per cent) than among women (20 per cent versus 17 per cent). Chart 8–1 shows how the percentages in Table 8–5 are related to those in Table 8–6. Moreover, by a rearrangement of columns two and three, this chart emphasizes a different aspect of Table 8–6: the sex difference by age.

In this graphic presentation of Table 8–6, the height of each bar represents 100 per cent of the respondents in the particular subgroup; the width indicates the number of persons in each of these groups. The dotted line represents the weighted average of men and women combined using breakfast food XX: 28 per cent among younger people, 20 per cent among the older ones. The solid lines show that in each age bracket there are more XX users among the men than among the women; but the sex difference is more accentuated among the young people than among

CHART 8–1

Use of Breakfast Food XX by Age and Sex

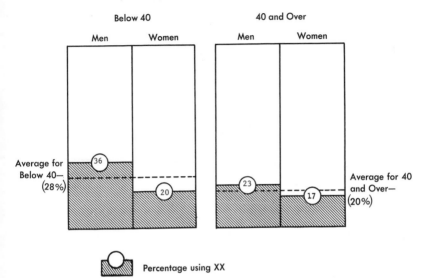

the older ones (36 per cent vs. 20 per cent as against 23 per cent vs. 17 per cent).

CORRELATIONS NEAR ZERO

Cases where the original correlation is zero or near zero are of special interest. Only by introducing a third factor may the interrelation of the involved factors become visible. Examine the cross-tabulation of age and listening to classical music in Table 8–7:

TABLE 8–7

Listening to Classical Music, by Age*

	Below 40	40 and Over
Listen to classical music	64%	64%
(Number of cases)	(603)	(676)

* This example is a modification of a table in Paul F. Lazarsfeld, *Radio and the Printed Page* (New York: Duell, Sloan & Pearce, 1940), p. 98.

Contrary to expectation, there is no correlation between age and listening to classical music. However, when education is introduced into the analysis as an additional factor, Table 8–8 is obtained:

TABLE 8–8

Listening to Classical Music, by Age and Education

	Below 40	40 and Over
College	73%	78%
(Number of cases)	(224)	(251)
Below college	61%	56%
(Number of cases)	(379)	(425)

The various relationships are more easily seen in Chart 8–2,

CHART 8–2

Listening to Classical Music, by Age and Education

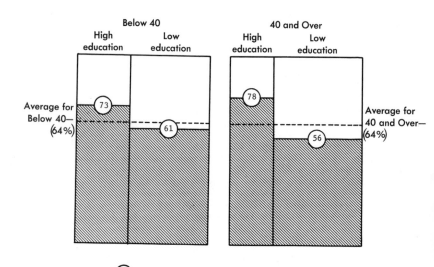

Percentage listening to classical music

The introduction of education as an additional factor reveals that there is, in fact, a correlation between age and listening to classical music. College-educated people listen more to classical music when they are older (78 per cent vs. 73 per cent). But it is just the other way around with people on a lower educational level: they listen more to classical music when they are young: (56 per cent vs. 61 per cent). If people are grouped by age, regardless of their level of education, these two tendencies tend to compensate each other, reducing the over-all difference to zero.

A similar, if more complicated situation is the substance of Table 8–9. It is based on a 1940 Gallup Poll designed to estimate the number of "isolationists," people who would have liked to see the United States not involved in what they considered a European war.

TABLE 8–9

Per Cent of Isolationists at Various Age and Economic Levels*

Age	Economic Status			
	Upper	Middle	Lower	Total
Under 30	30	28	22	26
30–49	21	23	26	24
50 and over	17	23	34	26

* Hadley Cantril and research associates, *Gauging Public Opinion* (Princeton, N.J.: Princeton University Press, 1944), p. 178.

From the Total column it would appear that age is not related to being an isolationist. The proportions vary only insignificantly (26 per cent–24 per cent–26 per cent). However if the influence of age is studied separately for each economic level, a distinct relationship appears. In the upper-income bracket the young people are much more isolationist than the old ones (30 per cent vs. 17 per cent); in the lower-income bracket the situation is exactly reversed (22 per cent vs. 34 per cent). In the

Total column these two tendencies compensate each other and produce a spurious pattern of noncorrelation.

A particularly interesting example of such a misleading non-correlation emerged from an experiment on the effectiveness of a headache remedy.[2]

The manufacturer of analgesic (A) was running short of one of the ingredients (x) that went into its making. In order to find out whether the absence of x made the analgesic less effective, 200 subjects suffering from infrequent headaches were treated in three successive two-week periods with three products on a rotating basis as follows: with the proper drug A, with drug A but lacking ingredient x, and with a placebo, an entirely inactive pill that had merely the appearance of a drug. The success of these three treatments was measured in terms of "percentage of relieved headaches" (Table 8–10).

TABLE 8–10

Effectiveness of Three Pills

	Per Cent Obtaining Relief
A	84
A lacking x	80
Inactive pill	52

The inactive pill had clearly a lower success rate than the two analgesics; but the difference between A and A lacking x was not statistically significant. On closer inspection, however, ingredient x did turn out to be relevant. The analyst justly reasoned that those patients who failed to react to the inactive pill would have been more sensitive test persons than those who professed that their headaches had been cured by the placebo. He therefore computed the success rates separately for these two groups, as in Table 8–11.

[2] E. M. Jellinek, "Clinical Tests on Comparative Effectiveness of Analgesic Drugs," *Biometric Bulletin of the American Statistical Association,* October 1946, pp. 87–91.

TABLE 8–11

Effectiveness of Two Analgesics Among Those Who—

	Reacted to Inactive Pill	Did Not React to Inactive Pill
	%	%
A	82	88
A−x	84	77

This difference now, between 88 per cent and 77 per cent, was statistically significant. It had been obscured by being mixed up with an insignificant difference in the other direction, among those unreliable test persons who reacted to the inactive pill.

AN ADDITIONAL FACTOR REVEALS LIMITING CONDITIONS

The refinement brought about by the third factor sometimes consists of revealing that certain correlations tend to disappear under special conditions, and correspondingly increase in the absence of these conditions. A study of France's suicide statistic showed the suicide rate (number per 100,000 population) to be 20 for Catholics and 40 for Protestants;[3] the suicide rate among Catholics is exactly one-half of the Protestant rate.[4] When the two denominations were further divided by their place of residence, the data in Table 8–12 were obtained.

TABLE 8–12

Suicide Rate by Religion and Size of Community
(per 100,000 population)

	Catholics	Protestants
Urban	31	38
Rural	9	41
Total	20	40

Table 8–12 shows that Catholics have a lower suicide rate irrespective of where they live, but the difference among Protestants is much more marked in the rural areas (9 per cent vs.

[3] From M. Halbwachs, *Les Causes du Suicide* (Paris: 1930), Chap. 4.
[4] See also the low suicide rate of Ireland in Table 2–2.

41 per cent) than in the urban ones (31 per cent vs. 38 per cent). Note that the data in Table 8–13 permit also a slightly different reading. Instead of making the comparison between Catholics and Protestants in different surroundings, one can compare the urban–rural difference among Protestants and Catholics. In Chart 8–3, the two arrangements, identical in substance, highlight these different aspects.

CHART 8–3

A. *Urban and Rural Suicide Rates by Religion*

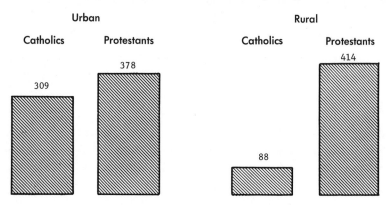

B. *Catholic and Protestant Suicide Rates by Size of Community*

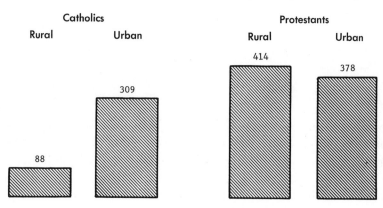

Clearly, the difference is sharper between Catholics and Protestants in rural areas than it is in urban areas (A), and the difference is sharper between urban and rural Catholics than it is between urban and rural Protestants (B).

THE ADDITIONAL FACTOR HAS AN INDEPENDENT EFFECT

Sometimes the third factor may turn out to have no effect on the original correlation, hence does not refine it. Instead it has an independent influence on the factor that in the original cross-tabulation was considered the *effect*.

If we introduce religion into Table 8–2, the pre-election poll result by economic status, we obtain Table 8–13:

TABLE 8–13

Election Poll in County X, by Economic Status and Religion
(per cent voting Republican)

	High economic status	Low economic status
	%	%
Catholics	27	19
Protestants	69	52

On each economic level, the Catholics produce less than half as many Republican votes as the Protestants (compare vertically), and within each religious group the higher economic strata produce more Republican votes than the lower strata (compare horizontally).

Again, it will be helpful to see the relationship between these four cells graphically, as in Chart 8–4.

The two graphs make it clear that both factors, economic level and religion, exert their influence more or less independently; hence, the proportion of Republican votes is highest among the well-to-do Protestants and lowest among the poor Catholics.

CHART 8–4

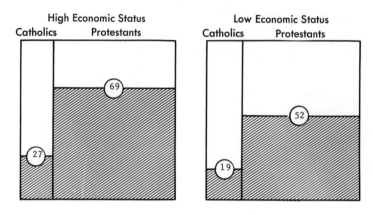

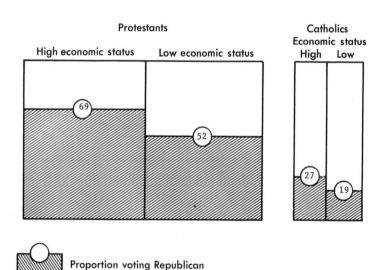

Proportion voting Republican

SUMMARY

The cross-tabulation, that is, the breakdown of a distribution into subgroups, is the most common device of survey analysis. This chapter discusses a preliminary function of the cross-tabulation, namely, the setting off of differences in distributions, by pin-pointing the subgroup in which certain measures reach their extreme values: In which population stratum is the Republican vote most concentrated? Who is most likely to listen to classical music? Which population segments have the lowest suicide rates? This refinement operation sets the ground for the step to be discussed in the next chapter: to discover *why* the differences occur at the points revealed by this refinement operation.

9

THE CROSS-TABULATION EXPLAINS

THE THREE examples of "refinement" that were discussed in the preceding chapter have one common characteristic: In no case is the additional third factor related to the causal factor in the original correlation. In the cereal example young age was a cause of eating more cereal; the third factor, sex, also affected the rate of cereal consumption. But while both age and sex were related to the crucial variable, the two were not related to each other:

Age—O—Sex

Eating more
cereal

Similarly, in the second example age and education proved to be related to listening to classical music but not to each other.[1]

If, on the other hand, a factor is to "explain" the correlation between two variables, it can do this only if it is also related to the factor considered as causal in the original correlation. The third factor derives its explanatory function from the fact that it is related to both factors of the original correlation, not just to one of them. Again an example will be helpful.

In Table 8–4 we found that male automobile drivers had more accidents than female drivers. In seeking an explanation for this correlation, so unflattering to the male ego, a third factor was

[1] Actually, in most populations age and education are related, the younger generation being as a rule better educated.

introduced to test the hypothesis that men have more accidents only because they drive more, not because they drive more poorly. Each of the two sex groups was divided into two sub-groups according to whether they drove more than 10,000 miles or 10,000 miles or less per year (Table 9–1).

TABLE 9–1

Automobile Accidents of Male and Female Drivers, by Amount of Driving

	Male Drivers		Female Drivers	
	Drove more than 10,000 miles	Drove 10,000 miles or less	Drove more than 10,000 miles	Drove 10,000 miles or less
Had at least one accident	52%	25%	52%	25%
(Number of persons = 100%)	(5,010)	(2,070)	(1,915)	(5,035)

The introduction of a third factor, *mileage driven,* revealed that the higher over-all accident rate of male drivers is entirely due to the fact that men drive more than women. If one compares men and women who had driven about the same mileage, the difference in accident rates disappears: It is 25 per cent for both men and women who had driven 10,000 miles or less, and 52 per cent for both men and women who had driven over 10,000 miles. Men have on the whole more accidents *because* they drive more. This can be seen from the bottom line of Table 9–1 which, in rearranged form, is once more presented in Table 9–2.

TABLE 9–2

Amount of Driving, by Sex of Driver

Drive annually—	Men	Women
	%	%
More than 10,000 miles	71	28
10,000 miles or less	29	72
Total	100	100
(Number of persons)	(7,080)	(6,950)

Seventy-one per cent of the male drivers are in the more-than-

10,000-miles group as against only 28 per cent of the female drivers.

Chart 9–1 presents Tables 9–1 and 9–2 in graphic form:[2]

CHART 9–1

Automobile Accidents of Male and Female Drivers, by Amount of Driving

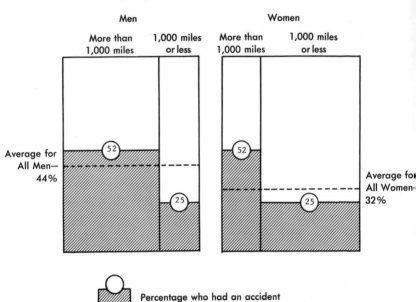

Percentage who had an accident

It will help to clarify the nature of this explanatory function of the third factor if we contrast the basic pattern of explanation, for which we have an example in Chart 9–1, with the basic pattern of refinement as represented by Charts 8–1, 8–2, and 8–3.

In terms of our graphic presentation, the difference between *refinement* and *explanation* is determined by the relative widths of the third factor (c_1 and c_2) with respect to (a_1 and a_2), as shown in the following Chart 9–2.

[2] For the sake of argument, here are two more constellations that could explain why men have more accidents than women: (1) men drive more recklessly, women more cautiously. (2) men drive more frequently in congested areas and during high-traffic hours, women in open areas during

CHART 9–2

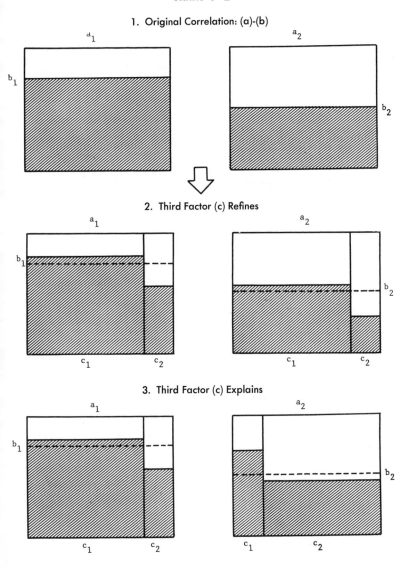

1. Original Correlation: (a)-(b)

2. Third Factor (c) Refines

3. Third Factor (c) Explains

low-traffic hours. In each case the explanatory third factor (reckless driving, driving in congested areas) is related to both factors in the original correlation.

If the ratio c_1/c_2 with respect to (a_1) is the same as with respect to (a_2), then the third factor (c) may only refine the original correlation (No. 2 in Chart 9–2). If the ratio c_1/c_2 differs as between (a_1) and (a_2)—then the third factor (c) may explain the correlation, provided (c) is also related to (b), the variable that is to be explained.

PARTIAL EXPLANATION

So far, we have discussed examples in which the third factor provided complete explanation. As things are in the real world, this will be the exception. As a rule, the third factor will provide *some* explanation, but not a complete one.

In a survey on factory absenteeism, it was found that married women had a higher rate of absenteeism than single women, as shown in Table 9–3.

TABLE 9–3

Proportion of Working Days Absent

	Married Women	Single Women
Absent	6.4%	2.3%
(Number of working days = 100%)	(6,496)	(10,230)

It occurred to the investigator that married women might stay away from work more frequently because they have more housework to do. In an effort to test this hypothesis, Table 9–4 was run.

TABLE 9–4

Proportion of Working Days Absent, by Marital Status and Amount of Housework

	Married Women	Single Women
	%	%
Have a great deal of housework	7.0	5.7
Have little or no housework	2.2	1.9
Total average*	6.4	2.3

* See line 1 in Table 9–3.

Table 9–4 indicates that the major increase in absenteeism is caused by the demands of housework, not simply by marriage. The absenteeism rate among married women is almost as small as that of single women if both have little or no housework, and absenteeism among single women is almost as great as that of married women if they too have a great deal of housework.

In a way, of course, it *was* marriage that increased absenteeism, because, as Table 9–5 shows, marriage brought with it more housework.

TABLE 9–5

Marital Status and Housework*

| | Married Women | | Single Women | |
	Number	Per Cent	Number	Per Cent
Have much housework	(5,680)	88	(1,104)	10
Have little or no housework	(816)	12	(9,126)	90
Total	(6,496)	100	(10,230)	100

* This table is merely a reproduction of the base figures on which the percentages in Table 9–4 are based.

Married women tend to stay at home more, because being married usually entails a greater amount of housework, but the explanation is not complete. Among the women having much housework, as well as among the women having little or no housework, the married women show a higher rate of absenteeism, the remaining difference being a fraction of the original difference shown in Table 9–3. This is an unexplained residual, for which there must be reasons other than housework, but related to marriage. Students may come up with some good guesses.

SPURIOUS CORRELATIONS

We turn now to a series of examples of a slightly different sort. Again, the third factor explains the original correlation, but it explains it by invalidating it at the same time.

Table 9–6 was obtained from a survey on candy eating. Again, marital status is the mystery attribute.

TABLE 9–6

Per Cent Eating Candy, by Marital Status

	Single	Married
Eat candy regularly	75%	63%
(Number of cases)	(999)	(2,010)

The same sample broken down by age instead of marital status yielded Table 9–7.

TABLE 9–7

Per Cent Eating Candy, by Age

	Up to 25 Years	25 Years and Over
Eat candy regularly	80%	58%
(Number of cases)	(1,302)	(1,707)

The first table suggests that single persons eat candy more regularly and the second table suggests that younger people eat it more regularly. However, since it is a commonplace that single people are on the average also younger, the question arises: Do married people eat less candy than single ones because they are *married,* and because husbands are less likely to buy candy than fiancés? Or, do married people eat less candy merely because they are, on the average, *older* than single people and have outgrown the taste?

We might guess either way, but the truth cannot be learned from these two tables. The data must be broken down, as in

TABLE 9–8

Candy Eating, by Age and Marital Status

	Up to 25 years		25 years and over	
	Single	Married	Single	Married
Eat candy regularly	79%	81%	60%	58%
(Number of cases)	(799)	(503)	(200)	(1,507)

Table 9–8, so that both factors, age and marital status, can be analyzed simultaneously. Graphically, this is shown in Chart 9–3.

CHART 9–3

Candy Eating, by Age and Marital Status

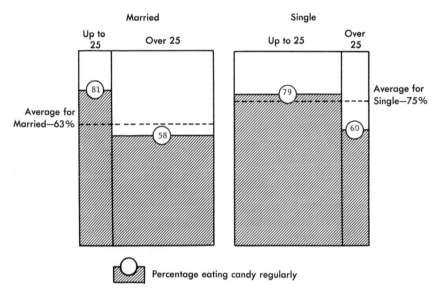

Percentage eating candy regularly

Table 9–8 and Chart 9–3 reveal that the relation between being married and eating less candy is completely explained by the fact that married people are, on the average, older than single ones, and that older people eat less candy. If married and single people of equal age are compared, the correlation between marital status and candy eating disappears; the figures clear the husband of all suspicion, or at least, of this one.

A PARTLY SPURIOUS CORRELATION

In the case of our candy-eating example, it was not difficult to find the true correlation, because the spurious one was based on a known fact—married people tend to be older than single ones. Unfortunately, the connections are not always so obvious.

An inquiry into the various characteristics of unemployed workers during the depression in the thirties revealed a strong negative correlation between the length of school training and the length of unemployment.[3]

Table 9–9 refers to the subgroup of unskilled male Negro workers about whom the point came out most clearly. The situation, however, was similar in all other groups.

TABLE 9–9

School and Length of Unemployment
(unskilled male Negroes)

| | Schooling | |
Length of unemployment	Up to 5 years	5 years and more
	%	%
Less than 2 years	47	52
2 years and more	53	48
Total	100	100
(Number of cases)	(6,054)	(6,039)

Men with better education seemed to have a considerably better chance of being unemployed for only a shorter period of time, and this seemed to be a perfectly satisfactory explanation. But when age was introduced into the analysis, the picture in Table 9–10 was obtained:

TABLE 9–10

Length of Unemployment, by Age and Schooling
(unskilled male Negroes)

	Schooling			
	Up to 5 years		5 Years and More	
Length of unemployment	Up to 35 years of age	35 years or more	Up to 35 years of age	35 years or more
	%	%	%	%
Less than 2 years	58	42	60	44
2 years and more	42	58	40	56
Total	100	100	100	100
(Number of cases)	(1,823)	(4,231)	(3,241)	(2,798)

[3] Katherine D. Wood, *Urban Workers on Relief*, Part I, Research Monograph IV (Washington, D.C.: U.S. Government Printing Office, 1936).

At this point the correlation between schooling and unemployment almost disappears. Age is the factor that affects the length of unemployment, regardless of educational level. The correlation of education and unemployment is for the most part only the spurious product of the fact that the better-educated workers are, on the average, of a young generation, a phenomenon that will characterize all countries in which the average level of education is on the increase. To be sure, age does not provide a complete explanation. There still remains a slight residual advantage accruing to those who have more schooling, which might properly be attributed to the benefits of education itself.

THE CORRELATION IS REVERSED

Table 9–11 illustrates some findings from a study of credit risks in installment buying.[4] One of the preliminary results was a table showing that higher-priced items constitute a better risk than lower-priced items:

TABLE 9–11

Bad Credits, by Price of Purchased Item

	Price Under $60	Price $60 and Over
	%	%
Bad credits	12.5	9.9
Good credits	87.5	90.1
Total	100.0	100.0
(Number of cases)	(4,303)	(4,088)

Table 9–11 shows that purchasers of high-priced items are better credit risks than purchasers of low-priced items. But when the size of the down payment was added as a third factor, a more complicated picture developed, as is shown in Table 9–12.

Purchases of high-priced items turn out to have a good credit

[4] David Durand, *Risk Elements in Consumer Installment Financing* (New York: National Bureau of Economic Research, 1941). The figures in this example represent a simplified result reported in that study.

TABLE 9–12

Bad Credits, by Price of Item and Size of Down Payment

| | Price Under $60, Down Payment | | Price $60 and Over, Down Payment | |
	Under $15	$15 and over	Under $15	$15 and over
	%	%	%	%
Bad credits	13.6	6.2	15.1	8.5
Good credits	86.4	93.8	84.9	91.5
Total	100.0	100.0	100.0	100.0
(Number of cases)	(3,655)	(648)	(890)	(3,198)

ratio only as long as they are accompanied by a down payment of at least $15. If the down payment is smaller, the bad-credit ratio is almost twice as high. And the low-priced items are also far from being all poor credit risks; as long as they too are bought with a major down payment, their bad-credit ratio is low.

Table 9–12 reveals in fact that the high down payment is a better index of the credit risk than the price of the purchased item. Moreover, if we compare high-priced and low-priced items in Table 9–12 on the same level of down payment, the correlation of Table 9–11 is reversed in each case; that is, it is the low-priced item that provides the lower bad-credit ratio: 13.6 per cent as against 15.1 per cent and 6.2 per cent as against 8.5 per cent.

A SPURIOUS NONCORRELATION

In a survey on milk consumption, it appeared that no correlation existed between economic status and the amount of milk purchased by each family during an average week (Table 9–13).

TABLE 9–13

Milk Consumption, by Economic Status

	Upper Economic Classes (A and B)	Lower Economic Classes (C and D)
Consumption	11.0 qts.	10.8 qts.
(Number of families)	(498)	(503)

The explanation of this surprising result was found when / size was taken into consideration as a third factor (Table 9–14).

TABLE 9–14

Milk Consumption, by Economic Status and Family Size

| | A and B | | | C and D | | |
	Families of 3 or less	Families of 4 or more	Total	Families of 3 or less	Families of 4 or more	Total
Quarts	8.0	17.1	11.0	6.2	14.4	10.8
(Number of families)	(334)	(164)	(498)	(281)	(222)	(503)

Now the situation is clear: The richer families of comparable size do consume more milk. But since the richer people have, on the average, smaller families, this reduced family size tends to offset the effect of the increased per capita consumption. This is the explanation of Table 9–13.

TRUE AND SPURIOUS CORRELATIONS

In two of our examples we labeled the originally established correlation as spurious, and it is now necessary to define the term with some precision. Why could we call the correlation between marital status and candy eating, or the noncorrelation between economic status and milk consumption spurious? Is it not a fact that any representative population sample will reproduce these relationships?

A good way to approach the issue is to look at both examples in which marital status was one of the factors in the original correlation:

1. Why do married women have a higher rate of absenteeism than single ones?—Because married women have more housework and more housework results in greater absenteeism.

2. Why do married people eat less candy than single ones?

—Because married people are, on the average, older, and older people eat less candy.

In our terminology, explanation (1) confirms the original correlation as *true*. Explanation (2) reveals the original correlation as *spurious*.

The difference can be pointed up by the peculiar relationship between the explaining factors, older age in example (2), and more housework in example (1), and the respective factor to be explained:

1. Married women . . . have more housework and therefore . . . stay at home more often.
2. Married women . . . are older and therefore . . . eat less candy.

In case (1) more housework is the result of being married and is, in turn, the cause of higher absenteeism. In symbols the relationship would read as follows:

getting married $\longrightarrow$ more housework $\longrightarrow$ more absenteeism[5]

The important point is that the relationship between "more housework" and "getting married" cannot be reversed. To have more housework will not result in getting married. In example (2) the position of the explaining factor, "getting older," is different. Getting older does result, on the average, in getting married, and also results in eating less candy. In symbols:

getting married $\longleftarrow$ getting older $\longrightarrow$ eating less candy.

Note the reversed position of the first arrow: "Getting older" is not only the cause of eating less candy but also the cause— not the effect of—"getting married."

[5] The arrows point in each case from the cause to the effect.

We say that the correlation with marital status was in (1) a true correlation and in (2) a spurious one. It is true when the explanatory third factor is asymmetrically connected with the two variables to be explained. It is spurious where the connection with the explanatory variable is symmetrical. In case (1) the explanatory factor (in the middle) is the *result* of the one variable and the *cause* of the other; in case (2) the explanatory factor is the *cause* of both variables.

The final test of the merit of this distinction between true and spurious correlations is a practical one. A factory manager, acquainted with the fact that married women stay at home more, might consider the desirability of discouraging female employees from marrying. Would such a policy, assuming it succeeded, tend to reduce absenteeism? The answer is—yes. Remaining single results on the average in less housework, and less housework means less absenteeism.

Suppose, however, that a candy manufacturer who learned of the relation between marital status and candy eating were to get a similar notion: that the consumption of candy would grow if girls were advised not to marry. Would his policy, again assuming he succeeded, lead to an increase in candy consumption? Here the answer is—no. Failure to marry does not keep girls young. And since only "not getting older" would keep candy consumption high, marrying or not marrying would have no effect on it.

Note, however, that the distinction between true and spurious cannot be made if all we have are statistical correlations. Whether the two arrows in the schematic presentation run parallel or point in opposite directions must be learned from an outside source. We know from experience, not from our statistical tables, that getting married does not affect a woman's age, but does affect the amount of housework she has to do.

The theoretical and practical reasons for distinguishing between true and spurious correlations are now clear: Only the true correlation reflects a causal connection; the spurious one does not.[6]

THE ROUTINE OF CROSS-TABULATION

We may take it for granted that students will, as a rule, try to distinguish between true and spurious correlations and thus aim at discovering causal relationships. But if this is their aim, they must observe an often violated rule: *Whenever a variable (1)[7] is cross-tabulated against other variables (2, 3, etc.) in order to discover the nature of their relationships, it is essential that the tabulations include all three variables simultaneously, if variables (2) and (3) are known or suspected to be interrelated.* Only from such a table is it possible to learn the true relationships that pertain among these three variables.

In analyzing survey results it is therefore advisable to determine in advance, as a matter of routine, which of the basic characteristics of the survey units are related to each other. Table 9–15 is a schematic example of such a routine tabulation.

In this sample the following factors appear to be correlated:

Age–marital status

Age–economic status

Religion–economic status

Often, these correlations will be known, even without special computations. Marital status and age will almost always be cor-

---

[6] The reader might care to consult the elaborate development of these questions in Patricia L. Kendall and Paul F. Lazarsfeld, "Problems of Survey Analysis" in *Continuities of Social Research,* R. K. Merton and P. F. Lazarsfeld, eds. (New York: Free Press of Glencoe, 1950). An interesting analysis of a special problem will be found in Peter M. Blau, "Determining the Dependent Variable in Certain Correlations," *Public Opinion Quarterly,* 1955, pp. 100–105.

[7] The term is here used not in its strictly mathematical sense (e.g., size, temperature, and so on), but is meant to include also what are technically called variations in attributes (married–single, eating candy–not eating candy).

TABLE 9–15

Cross-Tabulation of Basic Identification Data of a Sample of 1,000 Individuals

		Sex		Age		Economic Status		Marital Status		Total
		Male	Female	To 30	31–	A + B	C + D	Married	Single	
Age	To 30	175	175							
	31–	325	325							
Economic Status	A + B	200	200	100	300					
	C + D	300	300	250	350					
Marital Status	Married	350	350	100	600	280	420			
	Single	150	150	250	50	120	180			
Religion	Catholic	100	100	70	130	50	150	140	60	200
	Protestant	400	400	280	520	350	450	560	240	800
Total		500	500	350	650	400	600	700	300	1,000

▨ Related factors

related; younger people in this country have, on the average, a better education than older people who went to school at an earlier time of history; older people are, by and large, richer than younger ones because they have had more time to develop their earning capacity, and so on. Therefore, whenever, a distribution is analyzed by one of these factors (e.g., age), it is advisable to break the data down further and to analyze them simultaneously by the factor or factors with which the first factor (age) is correlated; in our example, economic status:

Age:	30 Years and Under		Over 30 Years	
	/ \		/ \	
Economic status:	A and B	C and D	A and B	C and D

For reasons of simplicity, we have in most of our examples described each factor as having only two alternatives: men–

women; high education–low education; 30 years and under–
over 30 years; had an accident–had no accident, etc. Some factors,
such as sex, actually do not have more than two alternatives,
but for most of the other factors this one-one split is arbitrary.[8]
Age differences, educational levels, and many others may be
divided into as many groups as seem suitable for the analysis.
This would not change the scheme essentially; it would merely
multiply the number of columns. For example:

Age: Up to 20 Years   21 to 30 Years   Over 30 Years
                 / /\ \   / /\ \   / /\ \
Economic status: A B C D   A B C D   A B C D

Finally, we shall do well to remember that cross-tabulation
may at times involve factors that are not clearly differentiated
by their label. Consider, for instance, the problem of comparing
opinions and attitudes of young people with those of their elders.
Obviously, there is an ambiguity in this comparison, because the
age difference may mean two different things: The younger people differ from their elders not only in that they have lived
fewer years, but also in that they have reached their age a
generation later in history.

An interesting method of separating opinion changes due to

TABLE 9–16

Separating in Attitude Surveys the Effects of the Two Aspects of Aging*

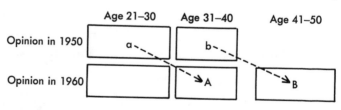

* After William M. Evan, "Cohort Analysis of Survey Data," *Public Opinion Quarterly,* 1959, pp. 63–72.

[8] See note 7 above.

age (= growing older) and to age (= history) was suggested in a study of age cohorts over time. The analytical scheme is shown in Table 9–16.

The age group 21–30 in 1950 (a) becomes in 1960 the age group 31–40 (A); (b) becomes (B), and so forth. Three comparisons can now be made:

(1) laterally $b - a$ tells what difference it made in 1950 to be 31–40 instead of 21–30

(2) vertically $A - b$ tells what difference it makes for the 31–40 years old to reach that age 10 years later

(3) diagonally $A - a$ gives, theoretically, the combined effect of (1)' and (2), that is of aging ten years *and* of having been born ten years later ($A - b + b - a = A - a$)

LIMITATIONS OF PROCEDURE

Once the need for cross-tabulation and its usefulness are established, the question arises as to how far this process should be carried.

There are first the obvious limitations of time and research funds; then, there is the obstacle of the lack of additional variables for tabulation and, closely connected, the limited size of the sample involved. Finally, the practical irrelevance of further refinements may pose limits to the process. The two obstacles mentioned last deserve more detailed discussion.

Since it is the purpose of cross-tabulations to discover significant differences, or nondifferences as the case may be, considerations of sample size become essential. However desirable a further breakdown may be, from an analytical viewpoint, the enterprise may become futile if the newly created subsamples are too small.

Suppose we wanted to introduce sex as an additional factor into Table 8–8, "Listening to Classical Music, by Age and Education." Then Table 9–17 would be obtained. Although these percentages seem to be different enough, they allow no conclusions because the samples from which they are derived are too small.

TABLE 9–17

Listening to Classical Music, by Age, Education, and Sex

	High Education				Low Education			
	Below 40		40 Years and Over		Below 40		40 Years and Ove	
	Male	Female	Male	Female	Male	Female	Male	Female
Listen to classical music	74%	69%	75%	82%	62%	60%	58%	54%
(Number of persons = 100%)	(110)	(114)	(134)	(117)	(186)	(193)	(207)	(218)

Refinement reaches a peculiarly frustrating stage once entire cells run out of cases and hence allow of no measurement. In that case, inferences about the empty cells are justifiable only if some general pattern of variability emerges that warrants projection to the empty cells.

PRACTICAL IRRELEVANCE

Sometimes the inquiry will stop because there is no point in going on in terms of the purpose of the particular inquiry.

Take the following example from a survey made for a drug manufacturer. He wanted to find out how consumer acceptance of his product in the southern states compared with its acceptance in the rest of the country. Table 9–18 answered this ques-

TABLE 9–18

Use of NN Drug by Area

	South	Rest of U.S.
Use NN drug	15%	21%
(Number of interviewees = 100%)	(5,398)	(16,862)

tion by showing that consumer acceptance of NN drug in the South was considerably lower than in the rest of the country.

If the question was asked merely to adjust manufacture and distribution to this lower demand, then this table is sufficient; the question is fully answered, and further analysis is unnecessary. Suppose, however, one were not content with merely knowing that the demand for this product is lower in the South, but wanted to increase it if possible. One then would want to know *why* demand in the South is lower. The pragmatic question would be this: Is the southern demand lower because of some intrinsic qualities of the South which a manufacturer cannot change, or does the cause lie with factors, such as distribution or promotion, which a manufacturer can attempt to change. To answer the question, Table 9–19 was constructed, introducing income as the third factor.

TABLE 9–19

Use of NN Drug, by Area and Economic Status

	South		Rest of U.S.	
	High	Low	High	Low
Use NN drug	32%	10%	30%	12%
(Number of interviewees = 100%)	(1,273)	(4,125)	(8,540)	(8,322)

As it turns out, buying patterns in the South are not different from those in the rest of the country: better-off people in the South buy as much of the NN drug as do their counterparts in the North, and the same is true for the less well off. The South buys less NN only because it has relatively more of the less well off than the rest of the country. Our manufacturer, therefore, has a clear answer to his question: The reason—lower income —is one about which he can do nothing.

SUMMARY

Under certain circumstances, a third factor, if introduced into a cross-tabulation, will explain the distributions in that table. The criteria for such an explanatory constellation are definable and clearly different from the refinement constellation (Chapter 8). There are two types of explanations: In one type the third factor explains by revealing the original distribution as spurious; the other type confirms the original distribution and provides a true explanation. Whether an explanation is of the one or the other type cannot be determined from the available numbers, only from outside knowledge about the relationship between these factors. To safeguard against spurious results as a matter of routine, it is advisable to tabulate simultaneously (not successively) all breakdowns of factors that are known to be correlated with each other.

10

REASON ANALYSIS I: THE ACCOUNTING SCHEME

THE QUESTION "Why?" may justly be considered one of the more powerful tools of research. Yet strangely enough, when we try to explain people's behavior merely by asking them why they did what they did, the results are disappointing. There are so many possible answers to the simple "Why?" that we have no way of knowing how all these reasons fit together, if indeed we could elicit them all in the first place. Suppose we asked some recent immigrants why they had come to the United States. Their answers would form a bewildering array of reasons. One will say: "We came because wages are low where we come from." Another "Our uncle convinced us that it would be better if we came here"; a third: "Because there are plenty of good jobs here in America"; a fourth: "My fiancé had come here some time ago, and I simply followed him"; and a fifth will simply say "Curiosity."[1]

It is not easy to see in what order one can put such a list of reasons because they are not only different in detail, but also with respect to the dimension of the decision process to which they refer. The first immigrant spoke of dissatisfactions with the old country; the second, of a person who influenced him; the

[1] Compare Sigmund Diamond, "Some Early Uses of the Questionnaire: Views on Education and Immigration," *Public Opinion Quarterly*, 1963, pp. 528, 541.

third, of the attractions of the new country; the fourth of a very personal constellation that decided the move; and the fifth, of a general motive. It is safe to infer that all these statements, except the fourth, are at best incomplete. If, for example, poor wages in the old country were a reason to move, then better wages in the new one are the necessary correlate; and the influential uncle must have given some reasons as to why he advised coming to the United States.

Clearly, people generally have more than one reason for their actions, and the simple "Why?" will ordinarily fail to reveal them all because of a natural tendency to explain our behavior with one reason rather than with a long and involved story.[2] To be sure, the abbreviated one-reason answer may have a significance of its own: It might sometimes reveal the one most important reason, a point on which we will have more to say later on.[3] The girl who followed her fiancé is a good example.

Asking for reasons, then, requires a more complicated apparatus, which generally involves the following five steps:[4]

1. Formulating the problem in terms of the specific research purpose
2. Selecting the type of action
3. Developing the accounting scheme
4. Searching for reasons
5. Assessing and interpreting statistics

The first three steps will be dealt with in this chapter, the remaining two in the next. With some modification, these five steps apply to a wide variety of situations in which we want to

[2] A classic example was the reply of Willie Sutton (America's most famous bank robber) to the question why he robbed banks: "Because that's where the money is."

[3] See p. 178.

[4] See the exposition in *The Language of Social Research*, Paul F. Lazarsfeld and M. Rosenberg, eds., (New York: Free Press of Glencoe, 1955), pp. 387–391.

know why a decision was reached or why a particular opinion is held. To illustrate the operation we will use examples that sometimes may seem trivial, ranging from casual everyday purchases to more considered decisions such as buying an automobile or casting a vote.

FORMULATING THE PROBLEM

At first glance it would appear that when we set out to explore a person's motives, we should approach our task with an open mind, that is, without first constructing a framework in which the various reasons and causes can be accommodated.

A moment's reflection, however, tells us that a person's whole life history lies behind even the simplest choice and that his entire social and physical environment is implicated in every one of his decisions. Since it is neither possible nor desirable to pursue all these reasons ad infinitum, the investigator must set appropriate limits to the inquiry. The boundaries of the frame eventually decided upon will largely depend on the purpose of the inquiry. The first step, then, is to formulate this purpose and to decide on the range of relevant factors.

Suppose we had been charged by some government agency with exploring the causes of immigration, with finding out what makes the United States attractive to immigrants, and what obstacles there are to immigration. In that case we would concentrate on all the "pulling" reasons of the move. But suppose, on the other hand, the old country had asked us to find out why so many of its families wanted to leave. In that case, our inquiry would primarily aim at the "pushing" reasons that drive the emigrants out.

Or suppose some crime commission wanted to learn how one could reduce the amount of burglaries in a community. Here one of the jobs would be to find out what circumstances lead men to become burglars: What factors in their background, their personal make-up, and the company they keep, lead them into such a career? But we shall also investigate how burglars select some targets and eliminate others as unsuitable; we should like to learn what makes some premises more burglarproof than others. Finally, we will want to know whatever we can about circumstances that have a deterrent effect.

Thus the purpose of the inquiry will determine the emphasis and will often lead to the important distinction between controllable and uncontrollable causes. In the immigration study, for instance, it might not be very interesting to learn that poor climate was a primary reason for the move, because there is usually not much one can do about it. Poor housing conditions, on the other hand, can be improved.

SELECTING THE TYPE OF ACTION

In our preview of the variety of reasons, we soon discern types of action that lead to a preliminary ordering of the data.

If we want to find out why people commit burglaries, we would soon discover that we might have to deal with at least two types of burglars: the habitual burglar whose last crime can adequately be explained only by reference to an earlier decision to become a professional burglar; and the second type, for whom this burglary was an isolated, if not the first, crime. Similarly, moviegoers fall into two broad categories with a great variety of subtypes in between: those who regularly go to the neighborhood theater, whatever the program, and those who go to the movies to see a special film they have heard or read about. Also our immigrants probably fall into two groups: those who take part in the primary decision, and those who—like the fiancée or children—simply follow the decision-maker.

Our learning of these varieties of types of behavior will come partly from our accumulated knowledge and common sense, but more often it will come from exploratory, informal interviewing. Once the research objective is formulated, this informal interviewing accompanies almost every research step until the final question schedule is evolved. Thus, the second step in our action analysis consists of deciding on the type or types of action we want to investigate, each of which will have its own accounting scheme.

DEVELOPMENT OF THE ACCOUNTING SCHEME

Once the multiplicity of reasons has been narrowed down to a manageable number, the next task is to map out, in preliminary fashion, the various dimensions of the action or attitude under study. By dimensions, we mean general categories of reasons, such as in the immigration example, dissatisfaction with the old country, attractions of the new one, personal influences, etc. Or, in a study of automobile purchases, the motives for wanting a new car in general, and the influences, such as recommendations and advertisements, which direct the purchaser toward a particular make of car. As long as specific reasons are bound together by the defining feature of such a single dimension, they are to be treated together, separate from reasons in another dimension.

The dimensions of reasons are abstractions from the testimony of a person, recounting how he happened to come to a particular decision. They do not have the immediacy of a personal recollection.

Their function indeed is to encompass the variety of individual reasons within a single logical framework so that the most general statement about the reasons for making a decision can be made in statistical terms. Idiosyncratic reasons have to be transformed into generalized categories.

A study designed to find out why women used a particular face cream, elicited this typical set of reasons:

MISS A: I heard the cream advertised over the radio.
MISS B: I have very oily skin, and this cream is supposed to keep it dry.

MISS C: I have dry skin, and the druggist told me that this would keep it moist.

MISS D: It was supposed to have a pleasant smell.

Two things are obvious, just as they were in our immigration interviews: one, that each of these respondents tells only part of the story we want to know; and second, that the answers belong to different dimensions of reasons. Some refer to the quality of the cream, some to how the respondent became acquainted with the cream, and some to the respondent's special needs for a cream.

From such an array of answers, we try to extract the different logical dimensions relevant to our inquiry. In our face-cream example, the following three reasons were developed:

1. Those referring to the *respondent*—special skin conditions or certain preferences or prejudices.

2. Those referring to the *product*—its qualities, its supposed effects, its price, and so on.

3. Those referring to the *source*—through which the respondent learned of the product or its qualities.

The preliminary exploration made it clear that a complete answer by any person to the question of why she bought the cream would now involve these three kinds of reasons—each referring to one of the three dimensions. Reviewing, in Table 10–1, the answers of the four respondents discussed above, we can see how incomplete they were:

TABLE 10–1

	Predisposition	Qualities of Cream	Source of Information
Miss A	No answer	No answer	Radio
Miss B	Oily skin	Keeps skin dry	No answer
Miss C	Dry skin	Prevents dry skin	Druggist
Miss D	No answer	Pleasant scent	No answer

Table 10–1 is an accounting scheme of the simpler sort: respondent's predisposition, qualities of the product, source of information. These three dimensions, slightly varied and generalized, form a sufficient accounting scheme for most of the simpler purchase propositions.

The more general form of the first dimension, *predisposition,* embraces all motives prior to the purchase decision. They range, depending on the object, from a desire to have more beautiful hands, to being less lonesome, or being more healthy. The second dimension refers to *attributes* of the desired object, and the third to the *influences* which affect the course of the decision. Stated even more generally, this set of dimensions involves the person, the object, and the social setting in which the person acts.

This then is a simple three-dimensional accounting scheme—in scientific parlance, a model that will fit many simple decisions in the market place and elsewhere.

Because such a set of relevant and sufficient dimensions permits us adequately to structure our replies for statistical bookkeeping purposes, we call it an *accounting scheme.* It is an integration of the dimensions identified in the preliminary interviewing into a small-size model which both guides the collection of information and provides the framework for its interpretation. Without such a generalizing device as the accounting scheme, individual decisions cannot be subjected to quantitative analysis; hence no generalizations can be made from them. It is the purpose of reason analysis to transform the individual reasons for a decision into more general, quantitative statements about decisions of that particular type and, ultimately, about decisions in general.

THE PUSH-AND-PULL MODEL

Whenever a change or switch from one situation to another, or one product to another is at issue, a model recommends itself that is based on the two poles of the decision: the dissatisfactions with the old situation or product (push) and the satisfactions expected from the change (pull). The decision to migrate or to move, which we discussed at the beginning of this chapter, is a good example; switching from one make of automobile to another, from one cigarette brand to another, are other examples.

Around this polarity of push and pull, other dimensions will form: the channels through which the new situation comes to attention and the influences that strengthen pull or push, as the case may be.

Influences, in turn, may have two subdimensions, the *channel* and the *content* of the communication. By relating these two, we shall be able to draw conclusions concerning the relative effectiveness of a message and the source from which it is communicated. At times, the source will be of no importance; for example, if somebody tells us that he acted so and so "because the war broke out." At other times it will be the source of the message that is important; for example, if a boys tells us, "I did this because father told me to."

The dimensions of the accounting scheme, whether only two or considerably more, are the basis of the subsequent data search and eventual statistical analysis. They must therefore exhaust the kinds of reasons expected, and they must be mutually exclusive, so that any reason can be clearly identified as belonging to one dimension and no other. Yet there is no limitation to the scope of the accounting scheme. The dimensions can be quite detailed or they can be very broad; they may describe only a limited aspect of a decision or they may cover the entire process.

THE FOUR DIMENSIONS OF TRAFFIC ACCIDENTS

Reason analysis, as we shall see in Chapter 11, is applied not only to interview data and conscious decision processes, but also to other actions and events, such as, for instance, to the analysis of accidents. We have called such reconstruction reason *assessment*.[5] In these efforts, the investigators of the traffic accidents have found the four-dimensional accounting scheme shown in Chart 10–1 to be useful:[6]

CHART 10–1

Accounting Scheme for Traffic Accidents

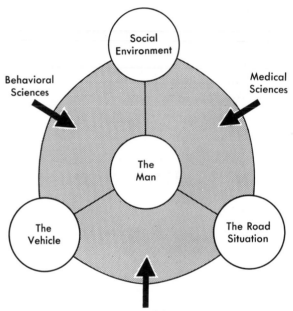

MULTIDIMENSIONAL MODELS

A rather complicated accounting scheme was required in exploring the reasons why lawyers for a particular criminal trial requested or waived a jury, to which their clients were entitled.[7]

[5] See pp. 112, 185.
[6] See *Case Studies of Traffic Accidents.* (Evanston, Ill.: Northwestern University, 1965), p. 5.
[7] The study was conducted as part of the Jury Project of the University of Chicago Law School, with the assistance of Howard Mann, then a student at the school.

We found two major types of such decisions: one, in which there was a standing rule in the lawyer's office either to waive or not to waive in a particular type of case. The second type of decision was made after more or less careful investigation of the circumstances in the individual case. It is for this latter decision that the following accounting scheme was designed:

Scheme of Reasons for Choosing Trial With or Without Jury

I. *Advantage Aimed At*
  A. More advantageous verdict
  B. Costs of trial
  C. Better prospects for bargaining or an advantageous guilty plea[8]
  D. Better opportunities for appeal
  E. Better insulation against client if case is lost
II. *Influences on Decision*
  A. Client's wishes
  B. Trial judge's preferences (to gain his favor)
  C. Counsel's personal preferences
  D. Countering opposing counsel's preference
    1. In particular case
    2. In general
  E. Tradition in the particular court
III. *Differences between judge and jury trial that can produce the advantage*
  A. Jury
    1. More than one man

---

[8] Under Anglo-American law, a defendant can avoid trial, or at least a verdict, by pleading guilty to the charged crime, often to a lesser offense, possibly even to an agreed upon sentence. The vast majority of prosecutions end this way. Cf. Harry Kalven and Hans Zeisel, *The American Jury,* (Boston: Little, Brown, 1966), pp. 18f.

      a. Composition can be modified through challenges before trial

      b. To convince one single juror might suffice[9]

      c. Individual bias cancels out

      d. No personal relationship to either side

    2. Basic attitudes

      a. Not always bound by rules of law

      b. Specific bias

        (1) for underdog

        (2) against unpopular indictment

        (3) represent popular prejudice

      c. Easier to influence

  B. Judge

    1. More lenient on penalty if jury waived

    2. Possibilities of personal bias

      a. Re counsel

      b. Re defendant or witnesses

      c. Re type of case

IV. The Case

  A. Content of case

    1. Type of offense

    2. Is the primary issue a question of fact or of law?

    3. Defense effort concentrated primarily on question of

      a. Guilt

      b. Sentence

      c. Major or lesser offense

  B. Expected length of trial

  C. Difficulty of case

  D. Personalities in case

    1. Client

      a. Personal background

---

[9] In most American jurisdictions, criminal jury trials require a verdict on which all jurors agree.

       b. Physical characteristics

       c. Manner of testifying

       d. Past record

    2. Witnesses

       a. Personal background

       b. Physical characteristics

       c. Manner of testifying

       d. Past record

  E. Estimated odds of success (prior to trial)

  F. Public attention received by case

A lawyer's reasoning for waiving a jury may then run as follows:

This was a case of a homosexual (IV-A-1); I was somewhat afraid of a jury, because they don't like sex deviates (III-2-b-3). Also, I know the judge; he is an experienced wise man, not one of those hot-rods (III-B-2-c). There was anyway only a small chance of acquittal (IV-E); the big question was whether I could get a suspended sentence (IV-A-3-b), and I found that judges are more lenient on the sentence if they try the case without a jury (III-B-1). On the whole, I thought I would get my client a better verdict without a jury (I-A). I talked to my client about this decision, but he left it to me (II-A).

THE ART OF ASKING "WHY NOT?"

At times the investigator wants to find out not what motivates action, but what motivates inaction. The aim may be to strengthen these motives if the action is undesirable, such as with crime, or to counteract these negative motives if the action is desirable. Prime examples of the latter situation are the birth control studies conducted in underdeveloped countries to determine why birth control is not practiced. We reproduce, in Table 10–2, an accounting scheme used for analyzing that specific inaction.

TABLE 10–2

*Accounting Scheme for Not Practicing Birth Control**

1. *Need*

(i) Exposed to pregnancy	(ii) Pregnancy undesirable	(iii) Either (i) or (ii) not present

2. *Knowledge*

(i) Of specific methods	(ii) That there are methods	(iii) Of neither

3. *Objections*

(to birth control in general and/or to specific methods)

(a) Substance	(b) Source
(i) Morals	(i) Religion
(ii) Health	(ii) Medical experts
(iii) Comfort	(iii) Family, friends
	(iv) Prior experience

4. *Availability*

(i) Physically unavailable	(ii) Psychological obstacles

* Modified from David L. Sills, "The Art of Asking 'Why Not?' " in *Proceedings of the Fourth All-India Conference on Family Planning* (Hyderabad, Bombay: Family Planning Association of India, 1961), pp. 26, 33.

Since all four dimensions—need, knowledge, absence of objections, and availability—must become operative to engender action, failure of one or all will impede it.

THE TIME DIMENSION

No decision is made at one instant of time; all extend over a time period. Even the most impulsive actions, such as an "impulse purchase" in a self-service store or a crime committed in a sudden flare of anger, can be meaningfully explained only in terms of preceding events. Time, therefore, is inherently a part of any decision process.

Not all accounting schemes include time as a dimension, simply because it is often without interest to learn the exact temporal sequence of a decision process. In purchase decisions of small items or in a lawyer's decision to try his case before a jury, the time dimension is of little interest. In other kinds of decisions, however, the time element will be an important factor. Normally, these will be decisions which extend over a longer span of time. The purchase of a major appliance or an automobile, the choice of the candidate for whom one will vote on election day, and a doctor's decision to begin prescribing a new drug require accounting schemes that include time as a dimension.

PREDISPOSITION AND PRECIPITATING EVENTS

There is a type of action, evolving over time, the end phase of which is triggered off by a relatively minor event. Latent motives for acting suddenly become effective when some external event or inner development activates the disposition and thereby forces the decision. The actions of our habitual pickpocket may be imagined in this way. The experienced pickpocket is always disposed to ply his trade; he actually decides to do so when some external event places him in advantageous proximity to a likely prospect.

For many purposes, this streamlined accounting scheme is adequate, especially when we seek to assess the impact of a purposefully designed influence such as an advertising or information campaign designed to stimulate immediate action.

But there is also a more flexible view of this dynamic problem. It envisages the possibility that people may be impelled to action not only through the triggering effect of some external event, but also by the force of some internal dispositions reaching a threshold of action by themselves. Crimes of passion can often be accounted for in this way. What appears to be an uncaused or inadequately caused burst of explosive violence in a person only appears so because we do not see any discernible event that we can charge with having tripped off the behavior. We do not see the strong emotions or motives feeding on themselves, as it were, until they reach the threshold of action.

This dynamic problem emerged nicely in a study that explored why some people switch from coffee to tea.[10] For some, there was a clearly defined external event, such as the sudden rise of coffee prices or an illness that was responsible for giving up one beverage for another. But there were a significant number of people for whom there was no such visible event propelling their change. Dissatisfactions with coffee had simply accumulated to the point where "something had to be done about it," without any apparent trigger from the outside.[11]

PHASES OF DECISION

Then there are decisions that extend not only over time, but change their character in the process. An analysis of the acceptance of newly developed drugs by the medical profession seemed to fit the basic predisposition, influences, and attribute model, but with a difference. Three distinct phases appeared to characterize the development. In the first, the *information* phase, the news is learned and absorbed; in the second phase the doctor is concerned with *evaluation*, and in the third phase, *confirmation,* the physician, prior to accepting the drug, looks for experiences of others. Table 10–3 shows how such a distinction of phases can provide insights into other aspects of the process.

The changing influence of channels, drug houses at first, and then professional sources, suggests that these sources have different functions in different phases of the process. Some decisions

[10] Phillip Ennis, *Why People Switch to Tea?* Bureau of Applied Social Research for The Tea Council of the U.S.A., Inc. (New York: Columbia University Press, 1954).

[11] The process during which the internal pressures accumulate is occasionally referred to as "crystallization," which is probably an unconscious echo of what is probably the finest example of an accounting scheme in literature: Stendhal's *De l'Amour,* in which the crucial and fatal phase of the falling-in-love process is named *cristallisation.*

TABLE 10–3

*Sources of Influence on the Physician at Different
Phases of the Decision Process* *

	First Phase	Second Phase	Last Phase
	%	%	%
Drug houses	80	56	45
Professional channels	20	44	55
	100	100	100

* Herbert Menzel and James Coleman, *On the Flow of Scientific Information in the Medical Profession* (New York: Bureau of Applied Social Research, Columbia University, 1955).

are best handled by an accounting scheme whose elements consist entirely of time phases. In the study of occupational choice, for example, the elaborate process of making up one's mind for a life work has been described in an accounting scheme of three phases of decision.[12] The first or *fantasy* phase, placed roughly in the age from six to eleven years, serves to determine the range of alternatives available to the child in which he explores them according to the pleasure they give him. The second phase of *tentative choice* (ages eleven to seventeen) determines the range of personal alternatives that the child considers. The last phase is the *selection of the specific occupation,* during which different influences come to bear to precipitate the final choice. This temporal organization of the accounting scheme allows the observer to see how different influences, such as family, school, and so on, operate at various times in the total process.

NARROWING THE CHOICE

A special case of these multiphase decisions is a process that moves from broad general delineations to ever narrower ones, suggesting an accounting scheme that chains a series of decisions of increasing specificity. This is an especially fruitful approach

[12] Eli Ginzberg, et al., *Occupational Choice, An Approach to a General Theory* (New York: Columbia University Press, 1951).

when the number of alternative choices is large. In a study designed, for example, to find out how disk jockeys selected phonograph records for radio broadcasting, it was realized that the number of possible records that might be chosen numbered in the hundreds of thousands. Yet, the disk jockey makes his actual selection of records in a very short time from among a limited group of records. How does he do it?

The developed accounting scheme permitted the tracing of this selection process from the almost unlimited variety to the final choice. The elements of the adopted scheme were the series of prior decisions, each of which had the function of successively narrowing the range of records down to a manageable number.

The first of these was the decision to be a particular type of disk jockey, a choice demanded by virtue of the conflicting pressures stemming from the industry itself. The disk jockey has essentially three alternatives. He can either be an *air salesman,* emphasizing that part of his work which deals with commercial sponsors; or he can become a *music promoter,* emphasizing his responsibilities as a popularizer or even creator of hit records; or he can become a *radio personality,* choosing to emphasize his job as entertainer for the listening audience. This decision in turn determines the audiences to whom he must appeal. The air salesman must try to reach a buying audience, the music promoter the teen-age public; and the radio personality must, through his program, select from a yet undifferentiated mass audience.

The next decision unit was the *type* of music to be played, a choice largely predetermined by the previous decision. The presumed musical tastes of his audiences dictated the proportion of "old favorites," "top hits," and new records to be used.

At this point, the cumulative impact of previous decisions had narrowed the range of acceptable records down to a small fraction of those the disk jockey might have chosen. At the same time these previous decisions also had the effect of determining the way in which the remaining records were sorted out by selectively exposing each type of disk jockey to different kinds of influences.

Another, more common accounting scheme of narrowing choices is standard for the analysis of major appliance purchases, but especially for the purchase of automobiles. Here the general decision to buy an automobile may be narrowed to a particular make, to a particular model, to a particular color combination, and so forth. To be sure, the sequence of these decisions might vary; the decision to buy another Buick might be made long before the purchase of a new car is decided upon; or the decision to have a convertible may indeed be the first one in the chain of narrowing choices.

SUMMARY

Within limits, appropriate questioning of the actors will elicit the motives of their actions. A necessary step in this process is the development of an accounting scheme, a model of the action to be explored. The scheme serves as a guide both to proper interviewing and to the subsequent statistical analysis of the data, and it is developed after preliminary, informal interviewing. The accounting scheme must take care both of the different time phases of an action and of the multiplicity of influences at any one time: it does it by establishing different *dimensions* within the action model. Many simple actions, especially purchase acts, will be adequately covered by the three-dimensional accounting scheme that allows for motives that originate in the actor, for influences from his surroundings, and for the properties of the object in question. There is also a discussion of more complicated accounting schemes.

11

REASON ANALYSIS II: DATA SEARCH AND INTERPRETATION

ONCE THE ACCOUNTING SCHEME is set up, the formal interviewing begins. This phase is to be distinguished from the informal, exploratory interviewing that must precede and inform the construction of the accounting scheme. It is well to recall at this point that the accounting scheme is but a logical structure designed to accommodate any set of actual reasons. The scheme is thus at the same time more complete than any real explanation pattern, but less concrete than the psychological reality of actual behavior.

The accounting scheme, therefore, must never be used directly as a questionnaire, unless its dimensions can easily be translated into question form. It would form so specific and rigid a question schedule that it would force the respondent to think in the analyst's terms instead of his own. On the other hand, if the interviewing proceeds entirely by loosely knit, open-end questions, it might fail to cover all the dimensions deemed relevant for the sought-for explanation.

The desirable solution is to ask first the general question "Why?" and supplementary questions in successive stages. For instance, in a questionnaire aimed at finding out why students selected a particular college, the following set of questions was used:

1.   Why, when planning your college years, did you decide for
_____ College?

2.   (*Supplementary questions. Ask only those which were not answered in 1.*)

   (A)   What was it about the college that influenced your decision?

   (B)   How did you learn about these particular qualities of the
college?

   (C)   Which of your own particular needs seemed to be taken
care of?

   (D)   To what degree did other persons influence your decision?

Some respondents would give a complete answer to question
(1); from others, only the supplementary questions would elicit
the total picture. Whether this is a difference of articulateness in
recalling the decision, or a true difference in emphasis is one of
the questions we shall come back to later on.[1]

PROBING

The major problem derives from the difference between what
the respondent thinks is a satisfactory answer and what the interviewer regards as satisfactory. The technique that can resolve this
difficulty is known as probing. The method essentially involves
the well-known art of cross-examination; yet since the interviewer
lacks the legal authority of an attorney, he must conquer through
tact and psychological empathy.

The problem arises in its simplest form when the respondent,
without knowing it, contradicts himself. A lawyer may tell us
that he insisted on a trial by jury in a particular case "because
I always prefer a jury." If then, upon specific questioning, he
recalls a case where he did waive his right to jury trial, the interviewer will be entitled to an explanation.

[1] See p. 177 f.

A more frequent and less obvious case arises when the answer is merely insufficient.

A good many million people have musingly watched one of the best probing interviews of this kind when they saw the lovely Katherine Hepburn as Jane in the motion picture *Summertime* quizzed by her admirer, the Venetian antique dealer:

JANE. Signor de Rossi . . . why did you come to see me?

DE ROSSI. It is only natural. You are not going to keep buying glasses every day.

JANE. No.

DE ROSSI. So I came.

JANE. But why?

DE ROSSI. Listen—two nights ago I am in Piazza San Marco . . . you are in Piazza San Marco. We look. Next day you are in my shop. We talk about glasses—we talk about Venice—but we are not speaking about them, are we? No. So last night I am in Piazza San Marco again. You are in Piazza San Marco again.

JANE. Half of Venice is in Piazza San Marco again.

DE ROSSI. But half of Venice was not in my shop this afternoon, or I would be a rich man.

JANE. I wanted to buy another glass.

DE ROSSI. That's all? . . . There are shops all over Venice. Did you look in any of them for your glass?

JANE. No.

DE ROSSI. You see?

JANE. But you said that you would find one for me.

DE ROSSI. And that's why you came back.

JANE. Yes.

DE ROSSI. No other reason.

JANE. Signor de Rossi, I'm not a child, but I don't understand.

DE ROSSI. Understand? Why must you understand? The most beautiful things in life are those we do not understand. When we spoke yesterday, I knew you were simpatica. Is that something you understand?

JANE. Yes. It means I am like a sister to you.

DE ROSSI. Miss Hudson—you ask me why I came here to see you. Because you attract me. Why? Because you do.

The general rule for probing is to recognize that the final choice is the end point of a funnel of successively narrowing alternatives. The interviewer traces back the reasons by which each alternative is eliminated except the final one. Conversely, any reason given for the final choice must preclude all other alternatives or be amended by additional reasons which—either singly or in combination—do so.

VERIFYING ANSWERS

Internal inconsistency and implausibility of given reasons will serve as warnings to the interviewer, but unconscious or deliberate reluctance might lead him astray. Moreover, memory fades with time and tends to be distorted by intervening events. Wherever possible, therefore, the interviewer should seek corroboration by appropriate cross-questioning, occasionally even by an independent search for objective data.[2]

Verification is especially needed when people report on such difficult questions as their exposure to various channels of information. People tend to underestimate, for instance, their own exposure to advertising and show reluctance to admit its influence. We cannot force the respondent to recall nor can we force him to admit. However, judicious questioning and solicitation of "playback" can reveal the extent to which the vocabulary of a particular advertisement or series of advertisements has been absorbed.

For influences of higher prestige, the opposite is often true. Respondents say they have read more books than they actually have, and overstate the highbrow magazines. An offer to buy all

[2] See Chapter 12.

old magazines in the house is still one of the better devices of verification.

The proffered, if incomplete, reason will sometimes serve as a signpost of the unexpressed reason. For instance, in the beverage study it was found that people expressed their reasons for giving up coffee in conventional and commonplace terms such as "It upset my stomach," or "It was too stimulating." But these replies formed the foreground to more emotionally laden attitudes of hostility to coffee which, though not stated as reasons, provided the latent impetus to giving up coffee. Identifying the themes—be it their underlying character or their superficial manifestations—is the function which reason analysis performs in such situations.

HOW FAR BACK SHOULD WE GO?

Interviewing for reasons involves at its minimum the enumeration of potentially relevant factors and the assessment of their importance. But sometimes it includes the additional step of tracing the immediate reason for action back to its origins, seeking as it were the reasons for the reason. Logically, we can link every factor to a prior one in a widening chain of causation that would end in a complete biography of the individual and a history of his environment.

How far back we should trace reasons depends upon the purpose of the research and the limits of the interview technique itself.

The analyst might care to stop his search for causes simply because he is not interested in further pursuit of the causal chain. Suppose we are making a survey of flower buying and Mr. X tells us that the last time he bought flowers was at the occasion of his wife's birthday. In this context we are unlikely to be interested in why he gave his wife flowers on her birthday: whether out of love for her and of flowers, whether as a routine performance that his secretary had to remind him of, or whether out of bad conscience—all these are variations, interesting in some contexts, but not in this one.

We might add here that also with respect to events that do not involve human actions, our curiosity to pursue the chain of causes is limited. An event is satisfactorily explained if it has been shown to be the result of a more general, known, and accepted proposition: "The Missouri River reached flood stage because upstream five inches of rain fell yesterday." We might or might not be interested to explore why there was such a heavy rainfall, but the rainfall *is* a full explanation of the flood.

Sometimes, it is only the more remote link in a causal chain that will require explanation. A while ago, an item in *The New York Times* aroused some merriment among its readers. It said: "There was an increase of 525 [in the number of unmarried, pregnant students in the New York schools] over 1961–62. The Bureau of Attendance had no explanation for the increase." It is all a matter of the right accounting scheme.

The boundaries of investigation will be reflected in our accounting scheme.

Often, however, we will *want* to pursue a causal nexus further, but the respondent is unable to do so, in spite of all the help we may give him by asking the proper questions; we cannot duplicate the psychoanalytic interview. This is the point where the technique of *reason analysis* reaches its natural barrier, and what is loosely called *motivation research* begins. Most often this will be true, for instance, when a reason has been pushed back to the level of individual "taste": "Why did you prefer the blue car to the green one?"—"Because I like blue better."

This is not the place to discuss this problem further; only the general direction of motivation research, taking off from here, may be indicated. Instead of the respondent's giving reasons, the analyst must develop and test his own hypotheses about the deeper layers of motivation. He may be guided in this search by his general knowledge of psychology, by pieces of information received from his respondent, or by both.

Part of the rapidly developing technique of so-called depth interviewing consists of guiding the respondent toward areas where the information he gives becomes helpful to the analyst for the formation of such hypotheses. Such areas, for instance, are biographical data and more specific instances of unexplained likes and dislikes. If time is not of the essence, the unguided association of the psychoanalytic interview will of course be the most fruitful source of motivational hypotheses.

PRIMARY AND SECONDARY REASONS

In a successful interview on any complex action, the respondent will give a variety of reasons; each dimension of the accounting scheme must have at least one answer; moreover within each dimension there may be more than one reason: not only did his father advise him to do it, but also his teacher, and also his brother.

Obtaining a variety of reasons reassures the interviewer as to the success of his exploration. But in another respect, this variety is unsatisfactory. If somebody acted on the advice of several people, one would like to know which, if any, was more influential than the others; one would like to know the relative importance of the reasons given, first of all, within the same dimension of the accounting scheme. And if the reasons fall into several dimensions, one would like to know which, if any, dimension was the most important. "We went to the movie because my girl friend wanted to see one and because I had heard good things about the picture at our theater." Was the good report as important a reason as his girl's wish?

The assessment of such relative importance may come from the actor-respondent himself, or from an observer, or from the analyst. The actor may be requested to rank the given reasons according to their importance, first within the same dimension; he then might make the same attempt with the dimensions themselves.

There is also a more radical way of testing this issue. The respondent can be asked whether, had reason X (and in turn reason Y) not existed, he would have nevertheless acted as he did. If the truthful answer is "yes" to the one reason and "no" to the other, the approach was successful. But often, it will be either "no" or "yes" to both questions, and it will not necessarily prove that both reasons were equally strong. Degrees of importance would not be revealed.

Sometimes the very sequence of the interview will reveal something about the relevance of reasons. On issues which are discussed without embarrassment, the first reason given may be the most important one. On touchy issues the reverse might be true. An observer or the analyst (who is something like a hearsay observer) may often do better in evaluating the relative importance of reasons than the actor himself.

At this point it will be useful to delineate our problem more clearly, both negatively and positively. It is not directly apparent why, if each of several reasons was a necessary condition of a completed action, one should have been more important than the other.

What is the common-sense meaning of one reason being more important than another?

The boy who went to the movies because his girl friend wanted to and because he wanted to see the particular film would conceivably admit that, had only the first motive existed, he would have gone anyway and thus react to the most discriminating test question. Failing to get the admission, the analyst himself might, after probing, decide to make this assessment.

But in the absence of such a radical test, relative importance might be derived from two other criteria, which two examples will help to illustrate. If we ask why the emperor of Austria declared war in 1914, we cannot well omit the murder of the crown prince in Sarajevo. And yet historians do not believe that this assassination was as important as other, broader political issues. What they mean, of course, is that the situation was such that a variety of other small and rather probable events would have provided the same trigger effect.

A reason might then be relatively less important because of two circumstances: it must be something like the straw that broke the camel's back, and there must be a great probability that if the particular event had not occurred, another incident would have taken its place in essentially the same chain of events.

A second illustration leads to a somewhat related point. It is taken from the already mentioned study of the American jury. It sometimes happens that a jury arrives at a verdict that differs from what the presiding judge thinks would have been the "correct" verdict.

Judges have told us in each case why, in their opinions, the jurys' views differed from theirs. One judge told us, for instance, that in a case before him he would have found the defendant, who had killed her husband, guilty of murder, whereas the jury convicted her only of manslaughter. He gave two reasons for the jury's leniency: The victim had openly consorted with another woman, and the defendant had a small child. The first of these two reasons, he thought, was the more important one. This assessment could have been based on a conversation the judge had with the jurors. If he had no such conversation, which is more probable, he was guided by his cumulative experience with juries in similar situations. The basis for this assessment is represented by the following hypothetical fourfold table. It gives the percentage of acquittals (or findings of guilty of a lesser offense than murder) for the four types of cases:

TABLE 11–1

Relative Importance of Two Reasons
(Figures are fictitious)

Motive of Homicide

Defendant —	Justified jealousy	Other motives
Had a small child	60% acquittals	30% acquittals
Had no small child	50% acquittals	20% acquittals

The cases in the upper left-hand cell represent homicide motivated by justified jealousy by a defendant who had a small child, and resulted in 60 per cent acquittals. The acquittal rate for the cases where the spouse had no reason for jealousy and no small child was only 20 per cent; and so on.

Having a child increases the percentage of acquittals by 10 per cent each time (from 50 per cent to 60 per cent; and from 20 per cent to 30 per cent); but the special motive of jealousy because of adultery increases the percentage of acquittals each time by 30 per cent (from 30 per cent to 60 per cent and from 20 per cent to 50 per cent).

Intuitively, there would seem to be a counter argument against the possibility of distinguishing more or less important parts where all are needed to sustain the whole. The simile of an automobile motor comes to mind. In what sense can one meaningfully say that the crankshaft is more important than the cable that connects the battery with the starter? Obviously both are equally essential to the motor's performance. But if we think of how much time and money are needed to replace the failing part, we could arrive at a meaningful yardstick of "importance."[3]

It is on considerations such as these that an assessment can be made in the individual case; for example, seeing the justified jealousy situation as more important than the defendant's being a mother.

While it thus seems possible, at least theoretically, to distinguish between more and less important reasons, a warning is appropriate as to the practical difficulties of making the distinction.

Yet, to the extent to which this can be done the advantage is considerable: In tabulating reasons, we will not have to give to the secondary reasons the same weight as we give to the primary ones. Another advantage lies in the simplification of cross-tabulation, if the motive for the action is to be related to some other variable. If each action can be classified under one (and only one) category, or at least under no more than two, the cross-tabulation is greatly facilitated.

PRESENTING THE RESULTS

Throughout Chapter 10 and thus far in Chapter 11, we have emphasized the necessity of classifying reasons into their proper dimensions. The accounting scheme guides the interviewer in his identification of all the factors involved in the decision, and in assessing their relative importance within each dimension. At that point, the various components have to be reassembled so that the action as a whole can be described and statistically presented.

---

[3] A stimulating discussion of some aspects of this problem will be found in Max Weber's "Critique of Edward Meyer's Methodological Views," in Max Weber, *On the Methodology of the Social Sciences,* E. A. Shils and H. A. Finch, eds. (New York: Free Press of Glencoe, 1949), pp. 113–188, especially pp. 166 ff.

TABULATING

After the interviewing is done and the reasons in each case determined, there comes the task of counting and summarizing, that is, the task of tabulating. The difficulty here comes from the variety of dimensions. Many a tabulation neglects dimensions and looks something like the one in Table 11–2.

TABLE 11–2

Reasons for Buying Face Cream

	Per Cent of Respondents
Recommendation	28
Beneficial to skin	21
Advertised	18
Saw it on the counter	15
Reasonably priced	10
Scent appealed	8
Because of special skin condition	7
(Number of respondents)	(250)

Clearly, there is disorder; some answers refer to the qualities of the cream, some to how the respondent became acquainted with the cream, and some indicate the respondent's special needs. Unless one has succeeded in singling out the one most important reason for each purchase—a difficult task, as we saw—the statistical presentation should reflect the several dimensions of the accounting scheme as Table 11–3 does.

Tabulating the reasons in this way allows us to see the relative frequency with which each item occurs within each of the three essential dimensions. The great number of "no answers" in this case reveals unsystematic or at least unsuccessful interviewing. We now have some idea of how the decision developed. We see that the final choice takes place as the result of several kinds of factors converging to produce the ultimate selection from alternatives.

TABLE 11–3

Reasons for Buying Face Cream

	Per Cent
Respondent's Needs	
Special skin conditions	7
No answer in this category	93
	100
Qualities of the Product	
Beneficial to skin	21
Reasonably priced	10
Scent appealed	8
No answer in this category	61
	100
Source of Information	
Recommendation	28
Advertising	18
Saw it on the counter	15
No answer in this category	39
	100

Table 11–3 reproduces the basic structure of the information; the actual yield from the individual interviews may, of course, be richer. Not only may one learn that there was a skin condition, but what the exact complaint was; not only may one learn that advertising was a source of information, but also what type of advertising it was; and so forth.

RELATING THE DIMENSIONS

By relating the answers in one dimension to those from another dimension, new insights can be gained. In the face cream study, for instance, one can show how the various properties of the face cream regarded as important were related to the sources from which the respondents learned about them. Such a table indicates just which two major arguments were successfully conveyed by the formal advertising media, television and print, and which arguments came through the informal channel of personal recommendation. This is done in Table 11–4.

TABLE 11–4

Source of Information About Various Properties of MM Cream

Properties That Attracted Respondent	Television	Printed Ads	Personal Recommendation
	%	%	%
Keeps skin smooth	62	1	2
Reasonably priced	13	1	43
One of the widest selling brands	17	25	47
Contains no harmful ingredients	—	10	—
Comes in smart container	—	56	—
Others	8	7	8
Total respondents	100	100	100
(Number of cases)*	(132)	(144)	(127)

* The total number of cases is greater than 250 because many respondents gave more than one source of information.

Similarly we might learn which arguments impressed which kind of customer by relating the arguments to categories of customers as defined by sex, age, and so on, or by more refined criteria, such as personality traits.

The example in Table 11–5 is again taken from the Chicago Jury Project. Before trial, counsel for both sides have a right to eliminate jurors whom they suspect of sympathy with their opponents' case. The accounting scheme developed for these decisions relates the qualities of the juror to the client's personality, to his case, or to the counsel himself as his representative. A lawyer might decide to reject a juror because he suspects that his ethnic background would make him unsympathetic to the personality of his client (A); or that the juror's low economic status might make him unsympathetic to the claims raised in this particular case (B).

REASON ASSESSMENT

Historically, the theory of reason analysis developed from the need to make detailed interviewing a useful tool of causal research, but the theory has broader applications. The accounting

TABLE 11–5

Eliminating Jurors Suspected of Hostility

		Dimension II: Expected to Affect Client		
Dimension I: Aspects of the Juror		(A) As defined by his personality	(B) As defined by his case in court	(C) As represented by his counsel
(A) Standard background characteristics	Ethnic origin			
	Occupation			
	Religion			
	Age			
	Sex			
	Economic status			
(B) Personality traits	Intelligence			
	Sympathy			
	Strength			
(C) Prior experiences	In similar case			
	General jury experience			

TABLE 11–6

*Analysis of Immediate Causes of 30 Accidents**

		Per Cent
Driver violations		35
excessive speed	20	
improper turns	10	
improper passing and others	5	
Driver errors		41
Car defects		5
Road properties		11
Miscellaneous		8
Total causes		100

* This is a slightly simplified version of a table reproduced in House Document No. 462, Part 2, 75th Cong., 3rd sess., January 7, 1938, p. 11. See also Stannard Baker, "A Framework for the Assessment of Causes of Automobile Accidents," reprinted in *The Language of Social Research,* Paul F. Lazarsfeld and M. Rosenberg, eds. (New York: Free Press of Glencoe, 1955), pp. 438–488.

scheme for traffic accidents, for instance, applies to events for which the evidence does not come primarily from interviewing but rather from observations on the scene of the accident, from tracks and traces that left clues as to the accident's probable causes. The method was first tried out on a series of thirty accidents, resulting in a table which is here reproduced (Table 11–6).

A slightly different version of reason assessment provided the principal data for *The American Jury*. There, the judge who presided over his respective jury trials formed an opinion—if the jury verdict differed from his own—as to why the jury came to a different decision.[4] The explanations are in terms of an accounting scheme that encompasses the peculiarities of the case, the person of the defendant, the predispositions and legal sentiments of the jury, the power of counsel, and occasionally, facts kept from the jury which only the judge knew.

EXPOSURE, POWER, AND IMPACT

Tables such as 11–6, indicating the frequency with which certain types of events can be traced to a specific cause, give rise to an interesting consideration. Let us take the accidents that are caused by speeding, some 20 per cent of the total. These accidents are obviously the product (in the exact mathematical sense of the word) of two component factors: *exposure,* the extent to which cars are driving at excessive speed, and *power,* the extent to which those who drive at excessive speed had accidents as a result of it:

$$\text{Impact} = \text{Exposure} \times \text{Power}$$

The 20 out of every 100 accidents that are due to speeding could be the result of 1,000 cars driving at excessive speed, and 2

---

[4] See Harry Kalven and Hans Zeisel, *The American Jury* (Boston: Little, Brown, 1966), Chap. 7, "The Logic of Explanation."

per cent of them having an accident because of it, or of 400 cars driving at excessive speed and 5 per cent having an accident because of it, or of any other combination of the two factors which, if multiplied, will yield .20.

To know not only the size of the impact but also that of its two component factors is important. To reduce automobile accidents effectively, one would like to know whether speeding increases the odds of an accident considerably and only a few people speed—or whether speeding increases these odds only slightly, but very many people speed.[5]

CHART 11–1

Speeding as a Cause of Traffic Accidents

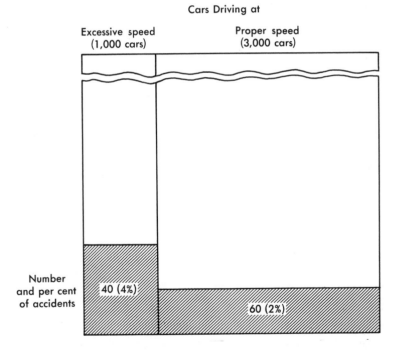

Cars Driving at

Excessive speed
(1,000 cars)

Proper speed
(3,000 cars)

Number
and per cent
of accidents

40 (4%)

60 (2%)

[5] Cf. a concrete analysis of this sort in Hans Zeisel, "A Note on the Effect of a Motion Picture on Public Opinion," *American Sociological Review*, 1949, p. 550.

We will now indicate how these measures of *impact, exposure* and *power,* gained through reason analysis, are in turn related to the data obtainable from survey operations.

We make here a forward reference to Chart 12–1[6] that co-ordinates reason analysis and controlled experiment, or its substitute, the survey cross-tabulation. Chart 11–1 illustrates this notion by giving a hypothetical paradigm of the relation-ships between speeding and accidents. The chart is to be read as follows: 25 per cent (1,000 out of 4,000) cars drive at ex-cessive speed; 4 per cent of them have accidents, as against 2 per cent of the cars that drive at proper speed. The difference between 4 and 2 per cent is due to excessive speed. In the termi-nology of the formula:

$$\text{Exposure} = 1,000 \text{ cars}$$
$$\text{Power} = 4\% - 2\% = 2 \text{ per cent}$$
$$\text{Impact} = 2\% \text{ of } 1000 = 20 \text{ accidents}$$

There is one other dimension that can be derived from a chart such as 11–1, namely, a measure of the *relative power* of the impinging variable, excessive speed in our example. Here it is the ratio of 4 per cent to 2 per cent. In words: Speeding doubles the chances of an accident.[7]

SUMMARY

The accounting scheme provides the structure of the ques-tionnaire, not its details. The question schedule itself, including

[6] See p. 196.

[7] A similar computation has been made concerning the power of a superior defense counsel in persuading a jury to bring in a verdict that diverges from the one the presiding justice considered correct. There *exposure* (how often was defense counsel superior to prosecutor?) was 9 per cent; *power* (how often is a superior defense counsel able to bring about a divergent verdict?) was 11 per cent; hence the *impact* was (.09 × .11 = 0.01) 1 per cent; in words: In one out of 100 trials the jury brought in a divergent verdict because of a superior defense counsel (see Harry Kalven and Hans Zeisel, *The American Jury* (Boston: Little, Brown, 1966), pp. 371 ff. and 479 ff.)

probing questions and questions designed to cross-examine, remains to be developed. A variant of the interviewing procedure (reason assessment) aims at obtaining nonverbal data from which individual actions can be reconstructed in analogy to reason analysis; the reconstruction of automobile accidents is a prime example. In the interpretation of reason-analysis data the intriguing problem arises as to whether one can meaningfully distinguish between more and less important reasons. Operational procedures for such a distinction are outlined. In addition, it is possible to assess in quantitative terms the impact of a causal factor by analyzing its two components: the frequency with which it enters the causal nexus and the power of its influence where it is present.

12

Triangulation of Proof

THE VARIETY of causes that determine human behavior make, as we have seen, the search for reasons and the efforts to assess their quantitative import forever a hazardous enterprise.

The assessment of causes is made with various degrees of uncertainty, and often these uncertainties can be measured in probabilistic terms. However, there is one constellation of proof that is of particular interest to the analyst, though usually the degree to which it reduces uncertainty cannot be measured: the confluence of proof from two or more independent sources.[1]

In the natural sciences, such corroboration is commonplace. Often a macro-observation, say, the Mendelian genetic law, is

---

[1] "No research method is without bias. . . . Once a proposition has been confirmed by two or more independent measurement processes, the uncertainty of its interpretation is greatly reduced. The most persuasive evidence comes through triangulation of measurement processes. If a proposition can survive the onslaught of a series of imperfect measures . . . confidence should be placed in it." E. J. Webb, et al., *Unobtrusive Measures* (Chicago: Rand McNally, 1966), pp. 1–3.

"The causal inference from different sets of empirical data are like pieces in a puzzle; they should combine to display a consistent total picture, and such an integration amounts to a check or test of the inference that is of essential relevance even if it does not . . . lead up to a numerical confidence level." Herman Wold and Lois Jureen, *Demand Analysis* (New York: Wiley, 1953), Chap. 2.5 (V)—"Triangulation" is a method frequently used in the estimation of economic parameters. Wold and Jureen derive, for instance, income elasticities from both family budget data and from price statistics over time.

confirmed by discovery of the corresponding micromechanism, in this case the genetic molecular process. Or, a theory based on retrospective data, such as the smoking–lung cancer hypothesis, is confirmed through experimental data, in that case by the induction of cancer into animals by the application of nicotine.

In the social sciences, the means of obtaining such a confluence of evidence is only in its infancy, and the art of producing it is still undeveloped. It should, therefore, prove useful to look at some of the possibilities.

We should perhaps begin with the type of corroboration that is derived from different phases of the same interview, engendered by probing and cross-examining on the part of the interviewer. In a survey of shopping habits, women would give as a reason for not buying in a particular store, that it was a "poor store." To check on the validity of that response, these same women, in a later part of the interview, were asked to evaluate that store on a variety of criteria. The number of specific complaints was then related to the frequency with which women had given "poor store" as a reason for not buying (Table 12–1); the expected relationship did obtain.

TABLE 12–1

*Verification of Given Reasons (I)**

Complaint Index (number of complaints)	Per Cent of Women in Each Group Giving "Poor Store" as Reason for Not Buying There
None	25
One	48
Two	64
Three or more	78

* From Paul F. Lazarsfeld, "Evaluating the Effectiveness of Advertising by Direct Interviews," in *The Language of Social Research*, Paul F. Lazarsfeld and M. Rosenberg, eds., (New York: Free Press of Glencoe, 1955), p. 411.

Sometimes verification can be obtained by more solid evidence. In a study of people's reasons for moving, some respondents gave as their primary reason that there had not been enough room in the old lodgings. Later they were asked whether the number of household members had increased prior to their moving. Table 12–2 relates the two answers.

TABLE 12–2

Verification of Given Reasons (II)*

| | Of Those Who Had | |
	Prior Increase in Size of Household	No Change in Size of Household
Proportion giving space limitations as main reason for moving	80%	30%

* From Peter Rossi, *Why People Move* (New York: Free Press of Glencoe, 1955), p. 144.

Here the reported motivation is verified by its high correlation with an objective fact: prior increase in the size of household.

Next we turn to a fairly frequent situation, where it is possible to check survey findings against data known from independent sources, such as census data, inquiry compilations, or company records.

The situation arises, for instance, when a survey is conducted to determine the share each competitor holds in a certain market. Such a survey, based on store or consumer data, will show figures such as those in Table 12–3.[2]

TABLE 12–3

Share of Various Brands of Tea Sold in the U.S. Market During 1966

Brand	Per Cent Share	Millions of Pounds Sold
A	51	(83.0)
B	18	(30.0)
C	12	(20.5)
D	8	(13.5)
All others	11	(18.0)
Total	100	(165.0)

[2] This is the type of information pioneered by the A. C. Nielsen Company but now provided also by a number of other companies.

The column that interests the client here is, of course, his per cent share of the market. But it is from the poundage figures that he can gauge the reliability of the survey operation, because he knows the pound figures, within limits, from his shipping records. After making allowances for time lag and changing wholesale and retail inventories, the accuracy with which the survey figure matches these shipping records will be a good measure of the accuracy of the share of market figures.

The point allows of generalization: Whenever possible, a survey maker should include one or two such reproducible items in his operation not because he wants to learn their magnitude, but rather because he knows them from an independent source.

A more complicated case of corroboration is presented in Table 12–4. Here, a brand-switching pattern is determined by comparing brand shares in two successive surveys. The difference between the two is then collated with the answers to a question in the second survey, designed to produce recall of these individual brand switches.

TABLE 12–4

*Consumption of Beers X and Y, as Reported in 1963 and 1965 Surveys**

	X	Y
1. Interviewees reporting in 1963 and 1965 the brand "drunk primarily"—		
1963	6.4%	7.5%
1965	8.8	6.4
Change	+2.4%	−1.1%
2. Interviewees reporting in 1965 "having switched since 1963"—		
From	16.3%	15.1%
To	19.1	13.2
Net balance	+ 2.8%	− 1.9%

* From a study conducted by Francis Van Bortel of Marplan.

We next report on a problem raised by a British government proposal to change the rules of criminal jury trials. Parliament was asked to remove the age-old requirement of unanimity of verdicts and allow henceforth 11:1 and 10:2 verdicts. The reform was designed to bypass the alleged one or two holdout jurors who could obstructively thwart the will of a solid majority of jurors ready to convict what might seem a clearly guilty criminal.

Since a few of the American states, notably Oregon, allow such majority verdicts by criminal-case juries, it was possible to predict tentatively what the new law would accomplish, or not accomplish, particularly the extent to which it could be expected to reduce the number of hung juries. It was possible, first, to compare the frequency of hung juries in these majority-rule states with their frequency in states that require unanimous verdicts. The figures were 3.1 per cent in majority-rule states versus 5.6 per cent in the others.

These figures suggested that allowing 11:1 and 10:2 verdicts would reduce the frequency of hung juries by somewhat over 2 out of every 100 trials; or, expressed in terms of all hung juries by (5.6 − 3.1 of 5.6 =) 45 per cent. But since the sample from which these figures were computed was small, and since trials in Oregon might be different from trials elsewhere, the basis for making the prediction was not strong. But then a second perspective on the problem became available, namely, the voting situation in which, in states that require unanimity, a mistrial was declared if the jury could not reach agreement (Table 12–5).

Table 12–5 shows that the 10:2 and 11:1 hung juries represent (24 + 10 + 8 =) 42 per cent of all hung juries. Since these are the majorities which, under the new rule, would be converted into verdicts, the 45 per cent reduction, calculated above from a completely different set of data, is strikingly corroborated.

There was yet a third set of data that had bearing on this issue. Some years ago, the state of New York abolished unanim-

TABLE 12–5

Vote at Which Juries Were Hung

Guilty:Not Guilty	Per Cent
11:1	24
10:2	10
9:3 to 3:9	58
2:10	8
1:11	–
	100

ity for jury trials in civil cases by allowing 11:1 and 10:2 majority verdicts. The Judicial Council for the state of New York counted the proportion of jury trials that ended in hung juries during the two years *prior* to the change of the rule (5.2 per cent) and during the six years *after* the rule was changed (3.1 per cent).[3] The reduction in the number amounted to (5.2 − 3.6 of 5.2 =) 31 per cent, a second corroboration from an independent source, albeit from civil cases, of the general magnitude of the reduction.[4]

REASON ANALYSIS AND CROSS-TABULATION

A different type of corroboration may come from collating the two standard approaches to causal analysis—cross-tabulation and reason analysis.

In theory, the two approaches must lead to the same result. For example, one of the questions that arose in the course of studying the American jury concerned the influence the lawyer

[3] Seventh Report of the Judicial Council, New York, 1943.

[4] These data stem from Harry Kalven, Jr., and Hans Zeisel, *The American Jury* (Boston: Little, Brown, 1966) and form part of an argument that was presented as contribution to the English debate by Kalven and Zeisel in *The Round Table,* April 1967, p. 158. See also the editorial page of the London *Times,* April 4, 1968. Majority verdicts are now the law in England.

had on the outcome of a jury trial or, more specifically, the difference it made for the outcome if either the prosecutor or the defense counsel was clearly superior to his opponent. Suppose we compared two strictly comparable groups of 100 trials, except that in the one group defense counsel was clearly superior to the prosecutor, whereas in the other the two were evenly matched, as is schematically shown in Chart 12–1.

CHART 12–1

*Superior Defense Counsel Causing Jury Acquittal
When Judge Would Have Convicted*

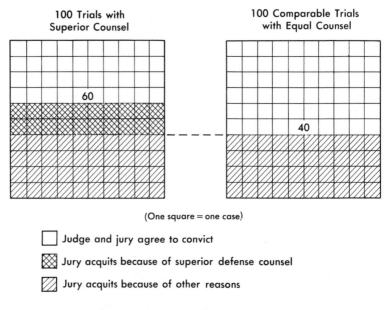

100 Trials with
Superior Counsel

100 Comparable Trials
with Equal Counsel

60

40

(One square = one case)

☐ Judge and jury agree to convict

▨ Jury acquits because of superior defense counsel

▧ Jury acquits because of other reasons

The graph reports for the equal-counsel cases 40 jury acquittals out of 100 cases in which the judge would have convicted; in the cases where the defense was superior, the number of jury acquittals is not 40 but 60. Since the two groups are assumed to be equal in every respect but one—superior versus equal counsel —we can infer that the difference of (60 − 40 =) 20 acquittals

TABLE 12-6

Effect of Superior Defense Counsel on Jury Disagreement
Where Judge Convicts

| | No Record/Stand* | | | | Record and/or No Stand† | | | | Total Cases |
| | Close‡ | | Clear‡ | | Close | | Clear | | |
	Sympathetic defendant§	Other§	Sympathetic defendant	Other	Sympathetic defendant	Other	Sympathetic defendant	Other	
Superior defense counsel	100%	74%	13%	30%	57%	38%	75%	13%	
Number of cases	(12)	(23)	(8)	(10)	(7)	(13)	(4)	(15)	(92)
Other counsel	70%	56%	35%	10%	59%	36%	48%	9%	
Number of cases	(61)	(136)	(48)	(231)	(22)	(100)	(25)	(274)	(897)
									(989)
Difference	+30%	+18%	−22%	+20%	−2%	+2%	+27%	+4%	
	X	X	X	X	X	X	X	X	
Number of superior defense cases	12	23	8	10	7	13	4	15	
Disagreements due to counsel	3.6	4.1	−1.8	2.0	−0.1	0.3	1.1	0.6	9.8

* Defendant has no criminal record and took the witness stand.
† Defendant revealed criminal record and/or did not take the stand.
‡ The evidence in the case was clear as to guilt—or it was close.
§ Defendant evoked sympathy—or not.

came about through the superiority of defense counsel in these cases.

And now comes the decisive step: Reason analysis too should reveal in these 60 acquittals that in 20 of them superior counsel was responsible for the acquittal. This is the basic scheme, denoting in theory the connection between cross-tabulation and reason analysis. It remains to be added that for this particular problem the confrontation was actually made.[5]

Table 12–6 gives the verdicts of jury and judge in 989 cases in which the judge would have convicted the defendant; 92 of these defendants had superior defense counsel; the other 897 defendants did not. The table makes the comparison between the two groups of cases. The table differs in one important respect from the schematic Chart 12–1: It compares eight subgroups instead of only two over-all groups. This is to maximize comparability between the two groups by subdividing it into more homogeneous groups.[6]

The last figure in the bottom line of Table 12–6 gives the sum of all jury disagreements due to counsel as derived from this cross-tabulation: 9.8, which is roughly 1 per cent of the 989 cases in which the judge convicts.

Reason analysis established that the equivalent of about 1 per cent of all jury acquittals came about because defense counsel in these cases was superior to the prosecution.[7]

[5] The actual situation is complicated by the fact that superior counsel may be but a partial reason in more acquittals, rather than the sole reason in the 20 trials.

[6] See p. 109.

[7] See Kalven and Zeisel, *The American Jury,* (Boston: Little, Brown, 1966), p. 370. Similar confrontation is attempted for other issues, such as the credibility of defendants, accomplice witnesses and so on. See Index under "Confrontation of methods." What was probably the first such confrontation of reason analysis and cross-tabulation appears in a 1938 study made by the Office of Radio Research, predecessor of the Bureau of Applied Social Research. It has been reprinted: E. Smith and E. A. Suchman, "Do People Know Why They Buy?," in *The Language of Social Research,* Lazarsfeld and Rosenberg, eds., pp. 404, 410.

SUMMARY

Since research findings, especially in the social sciences, are seldom totally conclusive, confidence is increased if the same finding is obtained independently from different approaches. Corroboration from different phases of an interview is one example; corroboration of survey findings through established census data another. It is suggested that whenever possible items be included in a survey that allow such corroboration. Corroboration of cross-tabulations through findings from reason analysis are the prime example of the general proposition that macro results can often be confirmed through investigation of the corresponding micro event.

13

The Panel

A GROUP of respondents that serves as a continuous source of survey information is called a panel. This arrangement grew out of needs which the one-shot survey could not answer, or could answer only poorly, and it has spawned its own peculiar research problems and techniques.[1]

The method of selecting a panel is not different from that of establishing its survey counterpart. In both cases it is a sample designed to represent a universe—of voters, of housewives, of doctors, of grocery stores, or simply of the general population. The distinctive point of the panel is its relative[2] permanence as a source of information at successive points of time.

[1] The first systematic presentation of this technique was published in 1938 in a paper by Paul F. Lazarsfeld and Marjorie Fiske, "The Panel as a New Tool for Measuring Opinion," *Public Opinion Quarterly*, 1938, pp. 596–612. The novelty of the technique concerns the observation and quantitative analysis of group behavior. Observations of *individual* development over time have long been practiced; first, of course, in botany and zoology; later in pedagogy (Pestalozzi), and more recently in genetics.

Probably the oldest systematic effort to relate group observations over time resulted in the first mortality statistics by John Graunt in 1662. To be sure, these first observations were made retrospectively from birth and death registries.

[2] Relative, because as time passes, some panel members drop out. On panel mortality see p. 236.

AMOUNT OF INFORMATION

One obvious advantage of a panel arrangement is the sheer amount of information that can be obtained. Single contacts in ordinary surveys have their time limits. Depending on the respondent's occupation, his interest in the topic, and the time and location of the interview, the outer limits of the interview will range from a few minutes to probably a maximum of two hours with a mode of about 15 to 20 minutes.[3] Whatever the limit, any effort to overstep it will result in interviewing failures and thus defeat itself.

Repeated contacts with the members of a panel—although they too have their limits—offer a much wider latitude and thus allow a much greater amount of data to be collected. The information, for instance, provided by a panel of housewives who record their daily purchases of packaged goods will provide an amount of data that will quickly require hundreds of punch cards per family.[4]

THE QUALITY OF INFORMATION

There is a second dimension along which the panel is superior to the one-shot survey. Whenever the desired information extends over time, the survey interview must rely on memory. With respect to some events, memory may be safely relied upon,

[3] In very special and rare cases a small sample of carefully selected interviewees might, of course, sit for several hours and even days. See generally, Herbert Hyman et al., *Interviewing in Social Research* (Chicago: University of Chicago Press: 1954).

[4] The first permanent consumer panel was established by Sam Barton in the United States. Consumer panels have now proliferated both in the United States and abroad. The first commercial panel operation, a panel of grocery, drug, and five-and-ten-cent stores became the core of the A. C. Nielsen operation. Strangely enough, in its standard reports, these store panels are used only as if they were successive independent samples.

even if the events go far back in time. Anybody can easily report, although he might not do it truthfully, the schools he went to, the recent sequel of his automobile makes, or his vote in the last election. But less significant events are quickly forgotten. The memory of a minor expenditure, or of a fleeting observation will disappear within days. Moreover, to rely on memory is always a treacherous undertaking, because of the unconscious and even conscious forces that tend to distort it. The question, for instance, "For whom did you vote?" asked one day after election day, will always elicit too many votes for the victorious candidate.

With the help of a panel conducted on behalf of a cigarette firm,[5] it was possible to determine the unreliability of such memory response. In the summer of 1959, the members of that panel were asked, among others, two questions: "What brand(s) of cigarettes are you smoking now?" and "What brand(s) of cigarettes were you smoking in the summer of 1958, a year ago?" By collating the answers with the brands *actually* smoked at that time, as known from interviews conducted a year earlier, the data in Table 13–1 emerged.

The 52 and 16 per cent of the smokers in the darkened cell reported correctly the brand they had smoked a year earlier. Only 4 per cent made the error of reporting a different brand when in fact they had smoked the same brand. But 28 per cent reported no shift when in fact they had smoked a different brand. There was thus a marked tendency to see one's behavior more constant than it actually was.

A related memory error concerning such time spans has been shown to recur with questions such as this: "Did you buy a new automobile during the last twelve months?" Invariably, the number of reported purchases is in excess of control figures, simply because such a pleasurable and important event is con-

[5] By Marplan, Germany.

TABLE 13–1

Memory vs. Fact

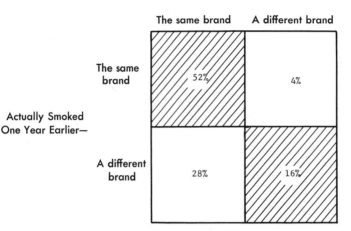

Total number of smokers = 2,386 = 100%

sciously or unconsciously squeezed into the response, even if it occurred thirteen or fourteen months before the interview.

Nor are projections into the future reliable. The question "Will you sell your car within the next six months?" can never mean more than: "Do you (now) think that you will sell your car, etc.?" The only sure way of finding out whether the car is sold within six months is to come back after that time and ask again.

Even if the critical event itself is correctly remembered, the subtleties of motivation and other details of the causal chain are as a rule lost to the investigator, unless they are traced while they happen or shortly thereafter.[6]

Thus, if we want to find out how a voting intention crystallizes

[6] Certain sophisticated types of analysis are based on panel data not because of their specific structure but because only a panel can provide data of such richness and detail; e.g., Lester G. Telser, "The Demand for Branded Goods," *Review of Economics and Statistics,* 1966, p. 300.

or changes during a campaign, how a television viewing pattern develops, or how a purchasing pattern is related to brand loyalty, the one-shot interview will seldom suffice. Only a panel will provide the full information.

CONCEPTS COVERING A TIME SPAN

The greater amount and the better quality of information which the panel yields is closely connected with another of its advantages. It permits a more accurate establishment of research concepts that are defined by behavior that extends over time.

We speak loosely of a *regular listener* or an *occasional user,* and in ordinary conversation the terms may stand. However, in an analytical study they require precise definition in terms of some frequency. Exactly where to draw the line between a *regular* and *occasional* user or listener will involve some arbitrary decision, but the panel can provide, at least, an exact record of how often and in what intervals the product has in fact been used, or a program listened to, on which the classification can be based.

We may take, of course, an interviewee's word or self-established record as to his proper classification, but we know that such reports are rough approximations at best.

SHIFTS AND CHANGES

Increased volume and reliability of the collected information are but the superficial assets of the panel. Its most interesting contribution goes to the *type* of information it provides.

To sharpen our focus, we will contrast the panel with the one-shot survey which, we will assume, provides information only over the relatively small time interval that precedes the interview. To trace changes over longer time periods would then require repeating the survey with a comparable but different cross-section. If the Gallup Poll wants to find out, for instance, whether the proportion of citizens who approve of President Johnson's policies has changed, it must arrange for a second, comparable national sample and repeat the questions from the earlier poll, as in Table 13–2.

TABLE 13–2

Shift in Approval of President Johnson's Policies 1965–1966*

	January 1965	January 1966
	%	%
Approve	74	58
Do not approve or are undecided	36	42
Total	100	100
(Number of interviews)	(1,500)	(1,500)

* Gallup Political Index, March 1966.

We learn from Table 13–2 that the proportion of people who approve the Administration's policies dropped from 74 to 58 per cent. No other aspect of this change can be learned from two such polls, except, of course, the comparable figures for sub-samples, such as the proportion approving among Democrats, Republicans, Negroes, women, voters under 30 years, etc.

Suppose now that instead of two successive polls, a panel had been established and the very respondents of the first poll had been reinterviewed. In that case we would be able to learn not

TABLE 13–3

Change in Approval of President Johnson, Hypothetical Case A

1966	1965		Total 1966
	Approved	Did not approve	
Approved	58%	—	58%
Did not approve	16%	26%	42%
Total 1965	74%	26%	100%

(1,500 interviews)

only the net balance of the shift but would also know *for every individual* where it stood at the time of the first and the second interview; a table like Table 13–3 could then be constructed.

Table 13–3 presents a cross-tabulation of the 1965 poll results against the poll of 1966. The two marginal lines at the bottom give the over-all result of the 1965 poll; the two right-hand marginal columns the result of the corresponding 1966 poll. So far, Tables 13–2 and 13–3 are identical; what distinguishes them is the fourfold core of Table 13–3, which allows us to see how the shift in the marginals from 74 to 58 per cent approval came about; these figures in the fourfold core of the table have been arbitrarily invented in order to illustrate a principle.

The upper left-hand cell contains the 58 per cent of all respondents who approved of Johnson in 1965 and still approved in 1966; the lower right-hand cell contains the 26 per cent who disapproved in 1965 and still disapproved in 1966. The only group that changed was the 16 per cent who approved in 1965 and disapproved in 1966; they account for the 16-point decline in approval from 74 to 58 per cent.

So that we can see more clearly the potentialities of such a switch table, we now add Table 13–4 (Shift Pattern B), the marginals of which are again the same as in Tables 13–2 and 13–3, but the core of which is quite different.

Table 13–4 was purposely designed to reflect another hypothetical extreme: here all the 26 per cent respondents who disapproved of Johnson in 1965 switched to approval in 1966; but a majority of the 74 per cent who approved of Johnson in 1965, namely 42 per cent of all respondents, shifted from approval to disapproval. The difference between these two shifts, 42 per cent to 26 per cent, results again in the net decline of 16 percentage points.

Tables 13–3 and 13–4 were laid out so as to represent the extremes of the internal shift patterns compatible with a marginal

TABLE 13–4

Shift in Approval of President Johnson's Policies 1965–1966,
Hypothetical Case B

	1965		Total 1966
1966	Approved	Did not approve	
Approved	32%	26%	58%
Did not approve	42%	—	42%
Total 1965	74%	26%	100%

(1,500 interviews)

change from 74 to 58 per cent. Since extreme constellations are always very improbable, the actual shift pattern surely lay somewhere in between.

TURNOVER AND NET CHANGE

We can now look more generally at the basic fourfold switch table, Table 13–5.

TABLE 13–5

The Basic Shift Table

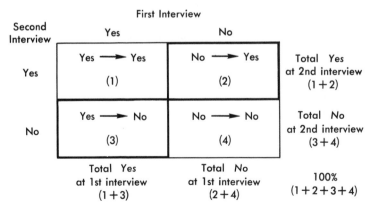

The upper left-hand (Yes ⟶ Yes) and the lower right-hand cells (No ⟶ No) contain those who did *not* change their position; the two cells along the other diagonal contain those who did change their position. The words "yes" and "no" in Table 13–5 stand, of course, for any dichotomy such as "use–don't use, know–don't know, and so on.

The two cells in the heavier frame (2) and (3), representing those who switched their position, can be combined so as to develop two crucial measures, *turnover* and *net change*. *Turnover* is defined as the proportion of respondents who shift their position, the *sum* of cells (2) and (3):

$$\text{Turnover} = \frac{(2) \ + \ (3)}{(1) \ + \ (2) \ + \ (3) \ + \ (4)}$$

It is 240/1,500, or 14 per cent, in Table 13–3 (Case A), and (630 + 390)/1,500 or 68 per cent, in Table 13–4 (Case B).

The *net shift* is defined as the *difference* between cells (2) and (3):

$$\text{Net shift} = \frac{(2) \ - \ (3)}{(1) \ + \ (2) \ + \ (3) \ + \ (4)}$$

The net shift in the cases of Tables 13–3 and 13–4 is of course the same, namely −16 per cent. Note that the net shift can be either positive or negative, depending on whether the figure in cell (3) is smaller or larger than in (2). Note also that while we have shown here how the net shift can be developed from panel data, this is a measure for which the panel is *not* needed; successive one-shot surveys produce it too.

MULTIPLE SHIFTS

The turnover need not be limited to a two-by-two table. The ensuing shifts can be more complex, as in Table 13–6, taken from one of the well-known studies of private finances that George Katona initiated at the Survey Research Center of the University of Michigan. It is based on a representative sample of U.S. families, interviewed first during the summer of 1964 and reinterviewed one year later.

TABLE 13–6

Per Cent of U.S. Families Holding Liquid Assets* of Indicated Size in 1964 and 1965

1965	None	$1–$1,999	$2,000–$4,999	$5,000 and over	Total 1965
			1964		
None	14	6	1	†	21
$1–$1,999	5	29	5	2	41
$2,000–$4,999	†	4	5	4	13
$5,000 and over	†	3	4	18	25
Total 1964	19	42	15	24	100%

* Checking and savings accounts, and nonmarketable U.S. government bonds.
† Less than ½ per cent.

The marginal distribution of families, in the bottom line and the last column, changes in no group by more than 2 percentage points: 21 per cent vs. 19 per cent, 41 per cent vs. 42 per cent, 13 per cent vs. 15 per cent, and 25 per cent vs. 24 per cent. But the internal turnover was considerable. The first column shows that 5 of the 19 per cent who had no assets in 1964 had some in 1965; and as the last column shows $(4 + 2 =)$ 6 of the 24 per cent who had assets of $5,000 and over in 1964 found themselves in 1965 in the two lower categories.

SHIFTS AT SEVERAL POINTS OF TIME

So far we have dealt with the shift picture in its simplest form: two alternatives at two different points in time. If the number of alternatives or the number of points in time (interviews) is increased, the shift picture becomes more complicated. Take, for instance, the shift arising from three panel interviews, to ascertain the extent to which voters approved the Administration's policy when the United States was at war against Japan. Two alternatives at three different points of time make for the eight possible shift combinations shown in Table 13–7, where the plus sign stands for the approval side of the dichotomy and the minus sign for disapproval. The per cent figures in the last column are based on an actual Gallup Poll conducted during World War II with a panel of 850 respondents.

TABLE 13–7

The Eight Shift Patterns for Three Successive Interviews

Shift Pattern	Interview I	Interview II	Interview III	Per Cent of Panel
1	+	+	+	56
2	+	+	−	8
3	+	−	+	11
4	+	−	−	5
5	−	+	+	7
6	−	+	−	2
7	−	−	+	5
8	−	−	−	6
				100

Table 13–7 allows us to answer an astoundingly large number of questions. To begin with: How many people did not change their position at all? The answer comes from groups 1 and 8: The 56 per cent who kept to approval, plus the 6 per cent who kept disapproving. What was the total approval at each of these interviews? Answer: For Interview I add 1, 2, 3, 4, which yields 80 per cent; for Interview II, add 1, 2, 5, 6, which yields 73 per cent; for Interview III, add 1, 3, 5, 7, which yields 78 per cent. In addition, we can count the turnover from one interview to the other, and thus give the summary picture of Table 13–8.

The data allow us to go one step further and show how the interview positions are related to each other. Table 13–9, shows nicely how the approval at Interview III is related to approval at

TABLE 13–8

Summary View of Shifts Between Three Interviews

	Interview I	Interview II	Interview III
Total approving	80%	73%	79%
Shift from approval at the preceding interview to disapproval	–	16% (3) + (4)*	10% (2) + (6)
Shift from disapproval at the preceding interview to approval		−9% (5) + (6)	16% (3) + (7)
Net shift from preceding interview		−7%	+6%

* Figures in parentheses refer to shift patterns in Table 13–7.

the two preceding interviews: Those who approved on both prior occasions show the highest percentage of approval at Interview III (88 per cent); the percentage is lowest (37 per cent) among those who approved at neither of the earlier occasions. The two groups in between reveal an additional insight: each of them approved only at one earlier period; but as one might expect, those who approved at the immediately preceding Interview II show a higher propensity to approve at Interview III (78 per cent) than those who approved only at Interview I (69 per cent).

TABLE 13–9

Relationship Between Interviews I, II, and III

Position at Interview III	Position at Interviews I and II			
	Approved at I and II	Approved at II only	Approved at I only	Approved neither at I nor II
Approved	88%	78%	69%	37%
Did not approve	12	22	31	63
Total	100%	100%	100%	100%
Share of total sample	64%	9%	16%	11%

None of these results could have been obtained from consecutive one-shot surveys, which never produce more than the marginal percentages of approval of 80, 73, and 79—that is, only the net shift.

A DYNAMIC TABLE

The usefulness of the panel is best demonstrated by a table that compresses data from a longer time period into a simple perspective. In this case, it summarizes the performance of three competitive marketing campaigns, conducted by three American manufacturers of detergents (Table 13–10).

TABLE 13–10

Composite Result of Three Detergent Campaigns as Derived from a Consumer Panel

	Brand A		Brand B		Brand C	
Estimated campaign budget	$9 million		$6 million		$3 million	
	↓		↓		↓	
Total all housewives	100%		100%		100%	
Proportion who tried the product	↓		↓		↓	
	45 = 100%		42 = 100%		26 = 100%	
	↓	↓	↓	↓	↓	↓
Became regular users	14	34	5	13	1	4

To begin with, the manufacturers of brands A and B were almost equally successful in persuading housewives to try their product, A more so (45 per cent) than B (42 per cent); C was considearbly less successful. But in relation to the cost of the campaign, the order of success was reversed. Measured in terms of how many housewives were persuaded by every $1 million to try their product, C succeeded best; A, least (Table 13–11).

It appears that C spent its dollars most effectively and A least effectively.[7]

The repeat purchases can be looked at in two ways: first in

[7] To be sure, there could be a ceiling effect: It might be more difficult and hence more costly to reach the fourth 10 per cent than the first 10 per cent of all housewives. See p. 10.

TABLE 13–11

TABLE 13–11

Campaign Success Measured in Terms of Housewives Reached per $1 Million Advertising

Brand A	Brand B	Brand C
$\frac{45\%}{9} = 5.0\%$	$\frac{42\%}{6} = 7.0\%$	$\frac{26\%}{3} = 8.7\%$

their relationship to the trial users, as indicated in the three short columns of Table 13–10. Of all those who tried their product, Brand A retained 34 per cent, Brand B 13 per cent, and Brand C 4 per cent. These percentages can be taken to reflect satisfaction with the product, and there the three brands differ sharply, in alphabetical order.

The over-all result: 14, 5, and 1 per cent of all housewives becoming regular users may then be thought of as the combined result of the effectiveness of the campaign and of the satisfaction with the product.

GAIN AND LOSS IN THE MARKET

At this point of our discussion, we shall look at a switch table that illustrates the weighty consumer decision of buying a new automobile. Table 13–12 is a record of the 272,107 transactions in the state of Michigan where the purchaser traded his old car against a new 1966 model. Hence we know for these car owners the sequence of two successive makes of cars.[8]

We have condensed the data so that the table singles out only three major makes—Chevrolet, Ford, and Plymouth—but also gives the combined number of cars sold by each of the four leading American car manufacturers. One limitation of these data should be noted: They record sales only where the pur-

[8] Through the courtesy of the Research Department of R. L. Polk & Company, which keeps a record of all automobile transactions and licensing operations throughout the United States. This is one situation where panel information is culled from existing administrative records.

TABLE 13–12

Old (Traded-in) and New Automobiles of Purchasers of 1966 Model Cars in Michigan

Purchasers Traded From

| Purchasers Traded to | General Motors | | Ford Motor Company | | Chrysler Corp. | | | | |
	(1) Chevrolet	(2) Other GM	(3) Ford	(4) Other Ford	(5) Plymouth	(6) Other Chrysler	(7) American Motors	(8) Foreign and Other Cars	(9) Total All New Cars
(1) Chevrolet	41,973	6,598	6,632	1,246	1,175	915	1,190	1,196	60,925
(2) Other GM	15,348	56,100	7,878	1,954	1,212	1,538	1,092	1,148	86,270
(3) Ford	8,411	5,353	35,133	3,402	1,487	1,150	1,312	1,949	58,197
(4) Other Ford Motor	1,289	1,859	3,514	6,884	175	310	173	214	14,418
(5) Plymouth	2,520	1,295	2,279	498	5,580	1,562	538	614	14,886
(6) Other Chrysler	3,191	3,511	2,869	814	2,771	9,727	603	629	24,115
(7) American Motors	537	419	486	134	136	108	3,453	258	5,531
(8) Foreign and other cars	1,156	932	920	199	229	173	214	3,942	7,765
(9) Total all old cars	74,425	76,067	59,711	15,131	12,765	15,483	8,575	9,950	272,107

chaser traded his old car to the dealer who sold him the new one. Car sales without trade-in are not recorded; hence the table does not contain purchases where the owner disposed of his old car in a different way, or purchased his first car. Finally, we note that this table refers to only one of the states and to only one year, the model year 1966. But since we aim here not at substantive findings but at patterns of analysis, these limitations of our data are not bothersome.

What can one learn from such a table? First, perhaps, the degree of brand loyalty. How many owners of a Chevrolet, Ford, or Plymouth stay with their brand?

From here on we shall refer to the various cells of Table 13–12 by the two-digit number that is obtained—as for areas on a map—by the column and row numbers that are added to the column and row and captions. Thus the first cell has number 11; the one next to it to the right, 12; and the cell in the lower right corner, number 99. Here, then, in Table 13–13, is the answer to our brand-loyalty question: Ford was first, Chevrolet close second, Plymouth poor third.

TABLE 13–13

*Loyalty to Leading Brands**

	%	Cell Number
Chevrolet	56%	(11)
Ford	59	(33)
Plymouth	44	(55)

* Each figure is calculated as a per cent of the column total in Table 13–12.

Next we might want to know the loyalty to the corporation (Table 13–14):

Plymouth loyalty is ahead of Ford because of the great loyalty of Plymouth owners to other Chrysler Corporation cars (22 per cent) as against a relatively low loyalty of Ford owners to other Ford cars (4 per cent). In corporation loyalty, Chevrolet leads the three: It has a brand loyalty almost as high as

TABLE 13–14

Corporation Loyalty of Leading Brands
(Buying either same or other car from same manufacturer)

	Brand Loyalty*	Loyalty to Other Cars of the Company		Total Corporation Loyalty	Cell Numbers
Chevrolet	(56	+	21	=) 77%	(11, 21)
Ford	(59	+	6	=) 65%	(33, 43)
Plymouth	(44	+	22	=) 66%	(55, 65)

* Figures are calculated as per cents of the column totals.

Ford (56 per cent) and a high loyalty to other GM cars (21 per cent), resulting in the high score of 77 per cent.

Next, in Table 13–15, we look at corporation loyalty by all those who trade cars of the particular corporations.

TABLE 13–15

Corporation Loyalty

	Loyalty*	Cell Numbers
	%	
General Motors	80	(11, 12, 21, 22)
Ford	65	(33, 34, 43, 44)
Chrysler	69	(55, 56, 65, 66)
American Motors	40	(77)

* Old and new cars in each cell as per cent of the particular column or pairs of columns.

General Motors car owners show the highest corporation loyalty. American Motors, the lowest. Although this is not the place to discuss the causes of these differences, we might nevertheless note that corporation loyalty is partly a function of the range of available cars.

The last set of derivative data from Table 13–12 is provided in Table 13–16. It gives the balances of cars one corporation took away from, or lost to, the other.

As the bottom line of Table 13–16 indicates, all manufacturers except Chrysler lose on balance in the trade-ins. Chrysler wins from all others (it has four pluses in its column); foreign and

TABLE 13–16

Shift Balance Between Corporations

To	From				
	General Motors	Ford Motor Company	Chrysler Corporation	American Motors	Foreign and Other Cars
General Motors	—	−798	+5,677	−1,326	−256
Ford Motor Company	+798	—	+3,338	−865	−1,044
Chrysler Corporation	−5,677	−3,338	—	−897	−485
American Motors	+1,326	+865	+897	—	−44
Foreign and other cars	+256	+1,044	+485	+44	—
Total	−3,297	−2,227	+10,397	−3,044	−1,829

other cars lose to all others (fifth column); General Motors gains from all but Chrysler (first column); and so forth. Such data, especially if seen every year for all states, and in more detail than we have presented them here, are of paramount importance to those engaged in the manufacture and sales of automobiles. In one way, however, these sales data are but the starting point for a more intriguing inquiry; namely, what moved 6,-598 families to abandon Ford for Chevrolet, others to move in the opposite direction, others from Ford to Chrysler, and so forth. Here we have a precise record of brand switches that constitute the ultimate aim of all manufacturers; hence we know precisely *where* to inquire what moved them—the most valuable information that manufacturers could wish to obtain. To unearth this information remains, of course, a most difficult task, but the panel technique offers a solid anchor point for its beginning.

WHO SHIFTED AND WHY?

The panel can approximate the controlled experiment better than any other survey operation. It permits relating shifts to prior exposures or nonexposures, as the case may be, and permits altogether precise focusing on individual behavior.

The panel cross-tabulation is not different from any other cross-tabulation. But because the panel provides as a rule more information on the causal chain than normal survey techniques, the panel can guard better against spurious correlations and provide insights superior to those derived from normal survey data.

Table 13–17 provides more data on the Willkie-Roosevelt Presidential campaign of 1940.[9] It relates vote intention in May to campaign exposure between May and August, and both to the resulting vote intention in August.

We begin with the top line of Table 13–17: in May 55 per cent of the voters intended to vote Republican, 45 per cent Democratic. Moving down one line, we find a measure of the reach of the two campaigns. The Democrats reached $10 + 15 = 25$ per cent of the voters "predominantly," the Republicans $32 + 17 = 49$ per cent, almost twice as many. Moving farther down, we have an effectiveness measure of the campaign, aside from the reach: 7 per cent of the Republicans reached by the Democratic campaign moved to the other side, but 20 per cent of the Democrats reached by the Republican campaign switched their vote intention; in addition, of the Republicans reached by the Republican campaign, 97 per cent stayed with the party, but of the Democrats reached by their party's campaign only 80 per cent stayed. Thus, on both counts—reach and power—the Republican campaign proved superior, resulting in an over-all net shift of 3 percentage points to the Republican side.

ASKING FOR REASONS OF SHIFTS

The second approach to discovering reasons for shifts is to ask the respondent why he shifted.[10] The panel offers here two

[9] See note on p. 118.
[10] See Chapters 10 and 11.

TABLE 13-17
Reach and Power of a Presidential Campaign

Vote intention in May	55% Republican			45% Democrat			Total
Predominant campaign exposure	10% to Democrats	13% to neither	32% to Republicans	15% to Democrats	13% to neither	17% to Republicans	100% (840)
Resulting vote intention in August							
% Republican	93	97	97	7	8	20	58
% Democrat	7	3	3	93	92	80	42
Vote intention in August	58% Republican			42% Democrat			
Net shift against May	+ 3 percentage points			− 3 percentage points			

special advantages: First, it provides a better opportunity than the normal survey for singling out those who have shifted; second, it provides valuable background information for the why questions, from earlier panel interviews.

The following data from the same Presidential campaign study will illustrate these advantages.

At the beginning of the presidential campaign, certain voters had not yet made up their minds. At that time, these undecided voters were asked which party they expected to win the election. Shortly before the election, they were reinterviewed about their vote intention. By correlating their expectation in May with their intention in October, the data in Table 13–18 were obtained.[11]

TABLE 13–18

Vote Intention and Expectation of Winner

Vote Intention in October	No Vote Intention in May but Expect Republicans to Win	No Vote Intention in May but Expect Democrats to Win
	%	%
Democrat	48	69
Republican	52	31
	100	100

Thus, without having asked "Why did you decide to vote Democratic (Republican)?" one of the reasons was established: People tend to vote for the candidate they expect to win.

This fact is commonly known as "the bandwagon effect." It is corroborated by what the respondents themselves had to say as to why they switched, for example: "I have always been a Democrat, but lately I've heard of so many Democrats who are going to vote Republican that I might do the same. Four out of five Democrats I know are doing that.[12] If the interviewing is

[11] *Ibid.,* p. 108.
[12] *Ibid.,* p. 109.

done to perfection, the entire difference of 21 percentage points should be explainable by such individual admissions of the bandwagon effect.

INCORRECT MEASURE OF EFFECTIVENESS

Before demonstrating how closely panel analysis can approximate the ideal of a controlled experiment, it will be useful to analyze here an example of the type of spurious evidence so frequently given as proof of a cause-and-effect relationship. Table 13–19 relates exposure to an advertisement to the use of the advertised product.

TABLE 13–19

Advertising and Use of Product

	Remember Having Seen the Advertisement		Don't Remember Having Seen the Advertisement	
	Number	Per Cent	Number	Per Cent
Use advertised product	(188)	30	(298)	21
Don't use advertised product	(434)	70	(1,150)	79
Total	(622)	100	(1,448)	100

Table 13–19 seems to give great credit to the effectiveness of the advertisement: The proportion of users is almost 50 per cent higher among those who remember being exposed to the adver-

TABLE 13–20

Product Use Before and After Exposure to Advertisement

	Used Product Before				Did Not Use Product Before			
	Saw ad		Did not see ad		Saw ad		Did not see ad	
	Number	Per cent	Number	Per cent	Number	Per cent	Number	Per cent
Used product afterward	(144)	72	(178)	71	(44)	10	(120)	10
Did not use product afterward	(54)	28	(74)	29	(380)	90	(1,076)	90
Total	(198)	100	(252)	100	(424)	100	(1,196)	100

tisement than among those who do not recall such an exposure (30 per cent vs. 21 per cent). Correct analysis of the panel data revealed this correlation to be misleading. The mistake of Table 13–19 is its failure to distinguish use of the advertised product *before* and *after* exposure to the advertisement, as in Table 13–20.

It turns out that the advertisement actually left no traceable effect upon its readers. The spurious correlation in Table 13–20 was obtained because the people who were users of the advertised product were more likely to notice the advertisements (198 out of 198 + 252 = 44 per cent) than those who had not been users (424 out of 424 + 1,196 = 26 per cent). The crucial element neglected in Table 13–19 but introduced in Table 13–20 is the time dimension.

The same type of fallacy may hide behind a variety of formulations. One, for instance, was hidden behind the proof that the size of the advertising budget for any group of corporations is positively correlated with the profitability of these corporations. The correlation is based on advertising expenditures and profits during any one year. The trouble with such a figure is, of course, that too many corporations—albeit imprudently—increase their advertising budget when profits are good and reduce it when profits are down.

CORRECT MEASURE OF EFFECTIVENESS

In discussing the relative merits of the controlled experiment we made a forward reference to a type of panel analysis that provides the closest survey approximation to a controlled experiment. Here then follows this analysis.[13] A cross section of 2,442 television set owners was interviewed in February and again three

[13] From Hugh M. Beville, Jr., *Why Sales Come in Curves*. Based on a study made by the Bureau of Applied Social Research for the National Broadcasting Company in 1953.

months later in May of the same year. Each time it was ascertained whether or not the interviewee had been viewing a certain program and whether he (or she) had been buying the product advertised on it.[14] Hence we had four possible viewing patterns and four possible buying patterns (Table 13–21).

TABLE 13–21

Viewing and Buying Pattern

	Viewing			Buying	
	In February			In February	
In May	Yes	No	In May	Yes	No
Yes	+ + continued	+ − stopped	Yes	+ + continued	+ − started
No	− + started	− − never listened	No	− + stopped	− − never bought

The + + individuals are those who continued, the + − ones those who stopped in the second period, the − + ones those who started in the second period, and the − − ones those who never listened or bought. Each individual then would have to fall into one of the four viewing patterns and one of the four buying patterns; by combining the two we obtain (4 × 4 =) 16 possible behavior (viewing and buying) patterns. Table 13–22 is this sixteen-cell table.

The (82) individuals in the first cell constitute those who

---

[14] Actually this table and the one that follows present not the figures for *one* program and the corresponding sponsoring product, but the average for 55 programs and 55 corresponding products, but the analytical scheme is not affected thereby.

TABLE 13–22

Viewing and Buying in February and May

(first symbol (+ or −) refers to February; second symbol (+ or −) to May)

| | Viewing | | | | | | | | |
| Buying | Continued (+ +) | | Stopped (+ −) | | Started (− +) | | Never Viewed (− −) | | Total Buying |
	Number	Per Cent	Number	Per Cent	Number	Per Cent	Number	Per Cent	
Continued (+ +)	(82)	12.0	(31)	9.8	(27)	9.2	(104)	9.0	(244)
Stopped (+ −)	(53)	7.7	(28)	9.0	(20)	6.8	(80)	6.9	(181)
Started (− +)	(57)	8.3	(24)	7.6	(24)	8.4	(81)	7.0	(186)
Never bought (− −)	(481)	72.0	(231)	73.6	(219)	75.6	(891)	77.1	(1,822)
Total viewing	(673)	100.0	(314)	100.0	(290)	100.0	(1,156)	100.0	(2,433)

viewed and bought in both periods $(++, ++)$; the second cell downward contains the (53) individuals who continued viewing $(++)$ but stopped buying $(+-)$; and so forth. The four columns of numbers are then also translated into percentages[15] from which several pertinent analytical statements can be derived.

We compare, first those (column 3) who *started viewing* the program after February $(-+)$ with those (column 4) who *never viewed* it $(--)$. In this way we can assess the effect of *having started to view*:

1. Gaining new buyers: Among those who started viewing 8.4 per cent started to buy, as compared with 7.0 per cent among those who never viewed, an increase of 1.4 percentage points or 20.0 per cent (1.4 over 7.0).

2. Holding old buyers: Among those who started viewing, 6.8 per cent stopped buying as compared with 6.9 per cent among those who never viewed, an increase of 0.1 percentage points or 1.4 per cent (0.1 over 6.9).

By combining effects (1) and (2), we can determine the over-all gain attributable to *having started to view* the program:

3. Among those who started viewing, the percentage of buyers increased from February to May from 16.0 per cent (9.2 plus 6.8) to 17.6 per cent (9.2 plus 8.4), that is, by 1.6 percentage points or 10.0 per cent (1.6 over 16.0).

4. Among those who never viewed, the percentage of buyers increased from 15.9 (9.0 plus 6.9) to 16.0 per cent (9.0 plus 7.0), that is by 0.1 percentage points or 0.6 per cent (0.1 over 15.9).

5. Hence, having started to view increased the number of buyers in that group by 9.4 per cent (10.0 minus 0.6) over what it would have been had they not started.

Similarly, by comparing columns 1 and 2, those who con-

[15] Considering viewing as the cause of buying; see Chapter 3 above.

tinued viewing with those who stopped viewing, we assess the effect of having continued viewing:

6. Gaining new buyers: Among those who continued viewing, 8.3 per cent started to buy as compared with 7.6 per cent among those who stopped viewing, an increase of 0.7 percentage points or 9.2 per cent (0.7 over 7.6).

7. Holding old buyers: Among those who continued viewing, 7.7 per cent stopped buying as compared with 9.0 per cent among those who stopped viewing, a decrease of 1.3 percentage points or 14.4 per cent (1.3 over 9.0).

By combining effects (6) and (7) we can determine the overall gain attributable to *having continued viewing* the program:

8. Among those who *continued* viewing, the percentage of buyers increased from February to May from 19.7 (12.0 plus 7.7) to 20.3 (12.0 plus 8.3), that is by 0.6 percentage points or 3.0 per cent (0.6 over 19.7).

9. Among those who stopped viewing, the percentage of buyers decreased from 18.8 (9.8 plus 9.0) to 17.4 (9.8 plus 7.6), a decline of 1.4 percentage points or 7.4 per cent (1.4 over 18.8).

10. Hence, continued viewing increased the number of buyers in that group by 10.4 per cent (3.0 plus 7.4) over what it would have been had they stopped viewing.

We can now move to the final step, the over-all evaluation of the effect of the television programs in terms of the added numbers of buyers of the advertised products as compared with what that number would have been without the television programs. In this operation we must consider not only the *effect* of started and continued viewing, as compared with stopped and never viewing—but also the *frequency* with which people started, respectively, continued viewing. We return, therefore, to Table 13–22 with the following consideration: had all the 290 people who actually started viewing (column 3) stopped (e.g., if the program had been canceled), they would have reacted as the 1,156 people who never viewed (column 4). The number of May buyers among the 290 were 51 (27 + 24); had this group of 290 not started viewing, there would have been 4 fewer buyers in it according to statement (5) above.

Similarly we can compute the loss of buyers among the 682 people who continued viewing (column 1) for the hypothetical case that they had stopped viewing as the 314 people (column 2) actually did. The 139 May buyers (82 + 57), had they not continued viewing, would have been reduced by 13, according to statement (10).

We now compare the three groups of figures in Table 13–23.

TABLE 13–23

Actual Buyers in February	Actual Buyers in May	Computed Buyers in May (*if program had not been available*)
425	430	413
The totals of lines 1 and 2 in Table 13–22 (244 plus 181). Expressed as percentage of the total sample (2433) this is	The totals of lines 1 and 3 (244 plus 186). Expressed as percentage of the total sample this is	430 minus the 17 (4 plus 13) buyers who would have been lost had the program been canceled. Expressed as a percentage of the total sample this is
17.5%	17.7%	16.9%

Thus the over-all effect of having had the program continued through May was an increase among buyers from the hypothetical 16.9 to the actual 17.7, an increase of 0.8 percentage points, or 4.7 per cent, over the February level.

REVERSAL OF CAUSE AND EFFECT

Our sixteen-fold table, relating viewing and buying at two different time periods, also permits investigation of a collateral

problem which had researchers often puzzled: the possibility that
there is not only an effect of viewing on buying (as we have
so far assumed) but also a reverse effect of buying on viewing;
that is, the possibility that buyers of a particular brand tend to
view the sponsor's program more frequently than nonbuyers.
Thus, there could be a *feedback* or *reinforcement* factor operating
that produces, or at least increases, the correlation found between
buying and viewing.

Two tests of the reinforcement hypothesis can be made with
our panel data by comparing February buyers and nonbuyers:

1. February buyers more than nonbuyers should claim that
they *started* viewing between February and May;

2. February buyers more than nonbuyers should claim that
they *continued* viewing the program after February.

A significant difference in the proportion of buyers and nonbuyers who report starting and continuing to view would be evidence that there is indeed, a reversal of intended cause and effect
operating within the data.

TABLE 13–24

	February Buyers	February Nonbuyers
(a) Number who were nonviewers in February	231	1,215
(b) Number of Febraury non-viewers who started to view between February and May	47	243
(b) as percentage of (a)	20.3%	20.0%

Test A: We test whether there are more claims of *starting* to
view among buyers than among nonbuyers. We divide the 1,446
nonviewers in February into two groups: those who were buyers
in February and those who were not. We then compute for each
group the proportion who report in May that they had started
to view between February and May. Table 13–24 reports the
result of this computation: No such effect is apparent.

If it were true that buyers had been more apt to start viewing than nonbuyers, a greater proportion of buyers should report starting to view during the three-month period. Actually, this proportion is the same for buyers and nonbuyers.

Test B: The other test examines whether proportionately more buyers than nonbuyers continue viewing. Here we take the 996 people who were viewers in February and trace their later viewing separately for buyers and nonbuyers (Table 13–25).

TABLE 13–25

	February Buyers	February Nonbuyers
(a) Number of viewers in February	194	793
(b) Number of February viewers who continued viewing after February	135	538
(b) as percentage of (a)	69.6%	67.8%

Here too the difference in viewing is insignificant. If reinforcement were operating we should find a higher proportion of continued viewing among the February buyers.

Since neither of the two tests shows a significant difference, we must conclude that there is no evidence of a reinforcement effect, causing buyers to view.[16] It is conceivable, though, that such reinforcement might operate with more substantial durable products, such as automobiles.

INCREASED STATISTICAL RELIABILITY

Since the maintenance of a panel is often more expensive than a succession of one-shot surveys with equivalent samples, it is essential to consider all aspects of the comparison between the two. One of them concerns the greater statistical reliability of a marginal over-all shift if registered by a panel, as compared with the same shift computed from two one-shot surveys.

[16] This situation is, of course, quite different from the one revealed in Table 13–21, where not the objective fact of viewing but the recall of an advertisement was the measure of exposure.

Suppose, for instance, two successive one-shot polls in Area A revealed an opinion shift from 60 to 55 per cent. And suppose that concurrently, a repolling of a panel of the same size in Area B revealed an identical shift from 60 per cent to 55 per cent. Can we say something about the statistical significance of the one difference as against the other? The answer is that a shift derived from a panel operation will as a rule have a higher degree of statistical significance than a comparable shift from two successive cross-sections. Put in another way: To produce a specified confidence interval, the panel will as a rule require a smaller sample than two independent cross-sections. The extent to which this will be true depends on the degree of correlation between the respective measures at time 1 and at time 2, and on this being a positive correlation.

BIAS FROM PRIOR INTERVIEWING

The very fact of having been interviewed once before about a given topic may influence the result of the subsequent interviews.[17] If the first interview brought the topic to the respondent's attention, his reactions thenceforth may become self-conscious and hence biased.

That this danger exists is clear, but just how great a danger is it? Generally speaking, the danger will be small if the topic is one which the respondent has been well aware of anyway. But if he had not thought about it before, the danger may be considerable.[18] The question is where between these extremes a particular inquiry will rank.

[17] To be distinguished from the possible "interviewer effect," continuing contact with a particular interviewer.

[18] This brings to mind the anecdote of the bearded man who when asked whether he slept with his beard above or below the blanket was unable to answer because he had never paid any attention to that problem; but from then on he had difficulty falling asleep because he could not make up his mind as to where to put his beard.

While experience and *a priori* estimates will always help, often there will be a need for more precise information on the magnitude of the reinterviewing bias.

The device for obtaining it is the controlled experiment, in which one group—the panel—is reinterviewed while in a corresponding control group the reinterview is omitted; or, the panel is interviewed periodically several times while the control group is interviewed only twice, once at the time of the first panel interview and again at the time of the last interview. Whatever differences are then observed between the two groups beyond the normal sampling error can be attributed to the interviewing effect.

Table 13–26 reports on a series of such experiments in which parallel questions were asked of a panel and in successive one-shot surveys of approximately twice the size of the panel. The main panel consisted of 425 respondents; three of the reported questions (1, 4, and 9) were based on a larger panel of 728 respondents.[19]

On the whole, the changes in the panel and in the control survey run in the same direction and are of similar magnitude; the rank-order coefficient of correlation is .77.

Three questions—3, 5, and 13—yield somewhat larger discrepancies. It is noteworthy that two of these questions are of the kind that are not likely to have occurred to the respondent prior to the interview; hence, on our theory, one might expect bias in the reinterview.

Experiments made to test the reliability of a panel used in the 1940 Presidential campaign confirmed the hypothesis that no significant differences between panel and control group are to be expected if the particular question is part of the general

[19] The study was conducted during World War II, between December 1941 and June 1942, by the Bureau of Applied Social Research at Columbia University in cooperation with the Gallup Poll on a grant from the Rockefeller Foundation.

TABLE 13–26

*Panel Changes as Compared with Corresponding Changes in
Independent Field Samples*

Question	Interviewing interval	Percentage refers to those saying:	Per cent change*	
			In panel	In control sample
1. "If Hitler offered peace now to all countries on the basis of not going further, but of leaving matters as they are now, would you favor or oppose such a peace?"	December to June	"Favor"	+5.6(1)	+ 5.0(3)
2. "So you think the U.S. is doing all it possibly can to win the war?"	February to June	"Yes"	+5.2(2)	+ 5.5(2)
3. "Whom do you consider to be the chief enemy: the German government or the German people, or both?"	December to June	"Both"	+4.6(3)	+ 1.8(6)
4. "If Hitler offered peace now, to all countries on the basis of not going further but on leaving matters as they are now, would you favor or oppose such a peace?"	December to February	"Favor"	+4.3(4)	+ 2.2(5)
5. "Are you satisfied with the conduct of the war against Japan?"	February to June	"Yes"	+3.4(5)	+ 8.0(1)

Question	Interviewing interval	Percentage refers to those saying:	Per cent change*	
			In panel	In control sample
6. "If Hitler offered peace now to all countries on the basis of not going further but of leaving matters as they are now, would you favor or oppose such a peace?"	February to June	"Favor"	+2.2(6)	+ 3.6(4)
7. "Whom do you consider the chief enemy: the German government or the German people?"	February to June	"German people"	+1.2(7)	+ 0.9(7)
8. "Do you approve of the President's home policy?"	December to June	"Yes"	+0.9(8)	− 2.8(11)
9. "Are you satisfied with the conduct of the war against Japan?"	December to June	"Yes"	−0.2(9)	− 0.7(9)
10. "Do you approve of the President's home policy?"	February to June	"Yes"	−2.8(10)	+ 3.8(12)
11. "Do you approve of the President's home policy?"	December to June	"Yes"	−4.0(11)	− 7.0(10)
12. "Are you satisfied with the conduct of the war against Japan?"	December to February	"Yes"	−5.3(12)	−10.5(13)
13. "Whom do you consider to be the chief enemy: the German government or the German people?"	February to June	"German government"	−6.7(13)	+ 0.4(8)

* The figures in parentheses indicate rank of change, in order of size and direction. Greatest positive change has rank 1; greatest negative change has highest rank 13. There are altogether 13 questions.

public discussion. No panel bias could be discovered on the following questions:

For which party's candidate do you think you will probably vote this fall?

Which party do you think will actually be elected?

What kind of President do you think Willkie would make: good, fair, or no good?

There is some evidence that prior interviewing, if it does not affect the *direction* of a change, may affect its size. In Table 13–26 the changes between the two independent samples were found to be somewhat greater than those within the panel. One might speak of a "freezing" effect of the panel. If the changes in the panel have, as they sometimes do, a greater magnitude than those in the control sample, we might speak of a "stimulating" effect. Something like it could be observed in the repeatedly quoted Presidential campaign panel of 1940. There each member was asked on six different occasions for whom he intended to vote. Table 13–27 shows one aspect of the change between the first and sixth interview in the panel, and the corresponding result for a control group that was interviewed only twice: once at the time of the first panel interview and again at the time of the sixth interview.

TABLE 13–27

Proportion Who Had Decided One Month Before Election for Whom to Vote

(of those who had not yet decided at time of first interview)

	Had Been Previously Interviewed 5 times	Had Been Previously Interviewed Only Once
Know for whom they will vote	60%	45%
(Number of respondents = 100%)	(213)	(214)

Repeated interviews seemed to have the effect of speeding up the process of deciding for whom to vote.

In 1941 the Columbia Broadcasting System set up a panel of radio listeners who were to appraise certain experimental programs. In order to see whether continued operation of the panel for as many as eight weeks would bias the attitude of its members, a field sample, matching the panel in four major characteristics, was set up. Again, as shown in Table 13–28, from the very beginning it appeared that the panel was slightly more critical in its judgment than the control group, whose "scores and ratings ran roughly 10 per cent higher than those of the panel."[20]

TABLE 13–28

Radio Program Scored by Panel and Control Group

	Average Rating	Score of Plot	Score of Talent	Score of Music
Panel	80.4	3.1	3.5	3.0
Control group	87.7	3.4	3.7	3.6

After eight weeks of operation, the relation of the panel and the control group had not changed. Just as at the beginning of the experiment, the panel was slightly more critical than the control group.

A somewhat more complicated experiment was designed to measure the effect of a preceding interview on three items: on the self-selection of a subsequent exposure (viewing a television program), on the evolving crucial attitude, and on the effect of that exposure on the attitude. Chart 13–1 depicts a scheme of this design.

By comparing (a) with (a'), (b) with (b'), and (c) with (c'), one can determine the influence of prior interviewing on the self-selected exposure. By comparing the relationship of

[20] Charles Harriman Smith, "The CBS Forecast Panels," in Paul F. Lazarsfeld and Frank Stanton, *Radio Research 1942–1943* (New York: Duell, Sloan & Pearce, 1944), p. 419.

CHART 13–1

*Measuring Interviewing Bias on Exposure and on the
Effect of That Exposure*

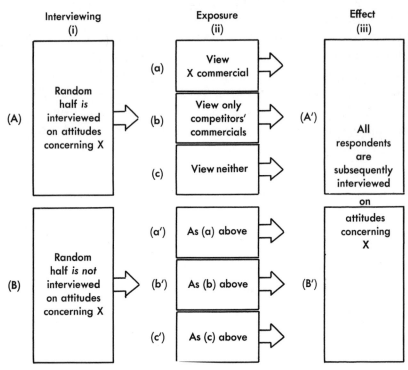

(a,b,c,) to (A′) with the relationship of (a′,b′,c′) to (B′), one
can determine the influence of prior interviewing on the effect of
the exposure on subsequent attitude; and by comparing (A′)
with (B′), one has an over-all measure of the combined effect
of these two possible influences.

PANEL BIAS AND MORTALITY

Almost any sampling of a human universe is bound to result
in some failures. Only nonliving matter allows perfect sampling.
Humans may be sick, or temporarily absent, or inaccessible, or

they may simply refuse to be interviewed. Such are the unavoidable deficiencies in the sampling of human populations. All these problems are aggravated in a panel operation. If the respondent is told that he will be interviewed more than once or that he is required to keep certain records, the rate of refusal is bound to increase. Even if he is left with the erroneous impression that this is only a one-time survey, the panel operation will have cumulative losses. At subsequent interviews, the losses that affected the first round of interviews—temporary absence and refusal to cooperate—are bound to recur. In addition, there will be losses specific to a panel, simply resulting from the elapsed time interval: Respondents will have moved or may have died.[21]

The problem created by the loss of panel members is twofold: first, the obvious cost problem, the loss of respondents on whom time and money have been expended. The more serious question is to what extent these losses threaten to bias the sample and, if so, whether there is a remedy against it.

There is no need here to deal with the bias problems of ordinary survey samples; they have been discussed elsewhere with sufficient care.[22] Our concern here is with the specific bias that may result from panel operations. A few generalizations garnered from experience with panel operations will have to suffice:

Losses from mobility occur more frequently among younger people than among older ones, and more frequently in larger communities than in smaller ones.

Losses from actual mortality affect, of course, primarily the oldest age brackets.

Temporary absence affects men more often than women, and more often the upper income brackets than the lower ones.

---

[21] To guard against loss through unreported moving, it is advisable to secure at the first interview names and addresses of relatives or friends, who later on might help to find the lost panel member.

[22] See "Nonsampling Errors," *The Encyclopedia of the Social Sciences* (New York: Macmillan, 1968).

Refusals to cooperate depend greatly on the type of cooperation required. If it is onerous, the normal refusal rate will be high unless a reward of some sort is offered. But the reward is then likely to be more effective in the lower income brackets.

Mail panels requiring literacy skills, however modest, suffer relatively greater losses in the lowest educational and income brackets. This bias does not necessarily evolve out of an initial refusal to cooperate; it may result from the subsequent failure to provide the promised cooperation.

RELEVANCE OF BIAS

Not every bias is necessarily fatal to all findings from a sample. It depends on whether the bias is related to the variable one wants to measure. To be sure, the trouble with bias is that one can never know in advance whether or how it will hurt. Nevertheless, sometimes bias may militate against part of the findings but leave others unaffected. For instance, a consumer panel designed to record the purchases of wearing apparel was found to underestimate the total consumption by a sizable degree. But the per-cent-share figures for the various types of apparel, and of the various types of fiber that went into them, were found to be remarkably reliable in spite of the over-all volume deficiency.[23]

SUMMARY

Obtaining continuous information from response units over time offers a variety of advantages: It increases the sheer amount of information; it increases the accuracy of the information by reducing the memory burden; it also permits a more precise

[23] An analogous situation was found in the course of our study of the American jury system: Here the sample grossly underrepresented most of the southern states. It reflected nevertheless with great accuracy the relative frequency of each crime—simply because that frequency did not vary by geographic region. See Harry Kalven and Hans Zeisel, *The American Jury* (Boston: Little, Brown, 1966), Chap. 3, "The Sample."

determination of processes, such as use habits that are derived from patterns that extend over time. Most importantly, the panel makes possible a sophisticated analysis of shifts and changes, and the tying up of these changes with prior events that have brought them about. Like all such tools, panel technique has its dangers: conditioning of the response units, and both actual and administrative mortality. But both these dangers can be guarded against. Thus the panel has become one of the more powerful tools of causal analysis.

INDEX OF EXAMPLES

243

INDEX OF CITED AUTHORS

247